P9-DEM-118

Louise Matteoni
Floyd Sucher
Marvin Klein
Karen Welch

THE ECONOMY CON

Oklahoma City
Indianapolis
Los Angeles

CURIOSITIES

Life was meant to be lived,
and curiosity must be kept alive.

Eleanor Roosevelt

When Jim White reached the ranch, he tried to tell the other ranch hands all about the wonderful things he had seen. He was very excited. He could hardly get the words out.

"There must have been a million bats!" he cried. "Maybe two, three million! They looked like a great cloud of black smoke!"

Everyone just grinned.

"Sure," said one. "You saw a cave with some bats flying out of it. We've all seen bat caves! But millions of bats! That sounds crazy!"

"There *were* millions of the bats!" cried Jim. "I watched for nearly three hours before they all came out."

"Come off it, Jim!" said another. "Three hours! It just seemed that long to you!"

"I tell you it *was* three hours!" Jim insisted hotly.

His friends just laughed and shrugged. They started toward the house. Jim followed them slowly.

They didn't believe him! He knew it was hard to believe his story. He knew that it sounded crazy. He *had* seen the bats, millions of them!

Deep in the Ground

A few evenings later Jim talked some of his friends into going with him to watch the bats fly out for food. His friends went along just to please him. They saw the cloud of bats. They heard the sound made by the bats' wings. They were as surprised as Jim had been.

Jim and his friends told people what they had seen. Still no one would believe the story.

41

dark-colored and smooth. Many of these figures formed solid poles that reached from floor to ceiling.

Jim and his friend could hardly believe that the things they saw were real. They stood and stared at the beauty of the rooms.

The two were so excited that they went on and on into the darkness. It was hard to move about. The rocky floor was hard to walk on. Water had worn it away so that it was rough. There were sudden slopes and drops. Sometimes the two had to use ropes to move from high places to lower ones. They often had to squeeze through narrow openings.

They were sometimes frightened at the thought of what they might find in the rooms. Now and then they could see huge shapes through the shadows. In the soft and changing light of their lamps each of these seemed to be a terrible monster, ready to leap upon them.

The day passed. The two did not return. Their friends began to worry about them. Jim and the boy were still going through the caverns.

They were scared. However, they were also excited by what they saw. They decided to stay and see how far the rooms went. Their food would last for another day. They would have to be careful, though.

They lay down to sleep on a bed of stone. Now and again the silence was broken by sudden notes of strange music. There was little sleep for either of them that night. After a few hours, they got up to search farther. The caverns seemed to go on and on.

At last they turned back. Their food would last only long enough for them to get back.

As time went by, Miyoshi caught more fish than she and her grandmother could eat. People from all over the village came to buy fish from Grandmother. Each day Grandmother would sit with her cane and a basket of fish in the cool shade of the tree near the door.

"Miyoshi must be able to think like a fish," Grandmother would say when someone asked how Miyoshi caught so many.

Often people would stay and talk with Grandmother after buying their fish. She was such a wise person that the people found she was able to help them with their troubles. However, they found that it was just fun to talk with her, too.

One day, when Miyoshi came home with a very large basket of fish, she saw her grandmother talking with a large group of people. The basket and cane were beside Grandmother's chair. Curled up next to the basket was a huge snake. No one seemed to see the snake as it picked up and ate fish after fish.

Miyoshi began to run and she called, "Grandmother! Look out for the snake!"

All the people ran away, leaving their fish behind. Only Grandmother stayed, and she shook her cane at the snake.

"Get away from my fish!" she cried.

Quickly Miyoshi changed herself into a pelican and flew to the snake. She flapped her wings around its head. She dove so close that she could feel its fangs brush the air beside her wings. Suddenly she fell to the ground and hopped away. She had broken a wing. That snake enjoyed eating birds more than it enjoyed fish. As it crawled to the forest after Miyoshi, it hissed and hissed.

"Miyoshi!" Grandmother called after she had gotten over the surprise of seeing Miyoshi change into a pelican. "Come back! You can't keep away from the snake for long

Vocabulary Review

On your paper write **a, b, c,** or **d** to show the item that best completes the sentence.

1. An ocean bank of sand or rocks is its _____.
   - a. water
   - b. shore
   - c. home
   - d. share

2. People who think quickly are clever, or _____.
   - a. greedy
   - b. dull
   - c. smart
   - d. small

3. A person who is weary feels _____.
   - a. tough
   - b. sweet
   - c. hateful
   - d. tired

4. A brilliant color is one that is _____.
   - a. broken
   - b. bright
   - c. blue
   - d. dark

5. To give someone praise means to give them a _____.
   - a. compass
   - b. compliment
   - c. fault
   - d. grace

6. To make a horse gallop is to make it _____.
   - a. rope
   - b. feed
   - c. groom
   - d. run

7. A plain is like a prairie; it is _____.
   - a. flat land
   - b. smooth water
   - c. hilly land
   - d. empty rooms

Books to Read

DeJong, Meindert   *The Wheel on the School*

Lina wonders why there are no storks in Shora. In her search for the reason and for a way to bring the storks to Shora, Lina also finds new friends.

Holman, Felice   *Elisabeth, the Treasure Hunter*

Professor Eckleberry helps Elisabeth's father arrange a treasure hunt on the beach. Elisabeth, her father, and Professor Eckleberry's grandson Charles find not one but two treasures.

Pinkwater, Manus   *Blue Moose*

Mr. Breton owns a restaurant on the edge of the woods. One day he finds a blue moose in his backyard and invites the moose inside out of the cold. The moose begins work as a waiter in the restaurant.

Selden, George   *Harry Cat's Pet Puppy*

Harry Cat finds a puppy and brings it home to the drainpipe in the subway where he lives with his friend Topper, the mouse. Soon the puppy is too big for the pipe, and the three friends begin a search for a new home for the puppy.

Uchida, Yoshiko   *Sumi's Special Happening*

Sumi tries to find the perfect gift for Ojii Chan, the oldest person in Sugi Village and one of Sumi's best friends. Sumi's search and the gift that she finds are real adventures.

DISCOVERIES

Something hidden. Go and find it. Go
and look behind the Ranges—
Something lost behind the Ranges,
Lost and waiting for you. Go!

Rudyard Kipling
from ''The Explorer''

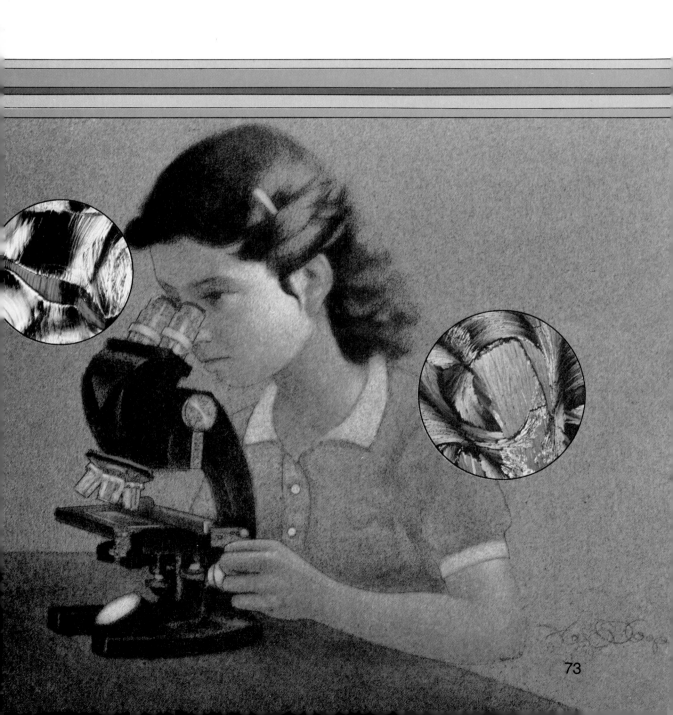

The Treasure of Sumiko's Bay

Barbara Chamberlain

People all over the world do many kinds of work to earn a living. Sumiko and her grandmother do a very different kind of work. They raise oysters so that they can sell the pearls. Sumiko discovers that many of the oysters are missing. Are fish killing the oysters? Are thieves stealing the pearls? This story tells how Sumiko uses her courage and cleverness to solve the puzzle.

Sumiko found the broken threads on her first dive into the warm water of the bay. For the last two months, the girl had found that a few valuable oysters were gone each week from their home on the rocky floor of the bay. Yesterday she tied thread across each of the bamboo poles that marked the oyster beds.

Sumiko came to the surface for air. She hung to the boat between the poles. "They came last night!" The girl knew every shell in the oyster beds. She checked them in their home every day to keep them safe from hungry shellfish. "It couldn't be anyone from my village," she told herself. "A thief must come in from the ocean, through the small open place in the mountains."

There was no other way to enter the bay. It was ringed on all sides by high mountains, the highest on the island of Okinawa. The mountains sat right in the water, except for one small beach below Sumiko's northern village.

The twelve-year-old girl swam to shore. She did not stop at the beach to say hello to anyone. She ran right to the home of the mayor of their small village. His house, with its gray roof, stood out among the sixteen other houses.

"A broken thread is not enough, Sumiko," Mayor Yamada told her. "A large fish may have done it, and taken the oysters as well. A strong pull from the waves could also have broken the threads."

only for your own food. However, I must protect the oysters. Whoever is stealing our oysters is throwing away the animals and selling the pearls. I must catch them! If only they couldn't get into the bay . . ."

There was a chance to do something! She raced home to tell her plan to Grandmother.

After their plans were finished, Sumiko and her grandmother spent five nights on the beach. They tried to sleep when they could. During the day Sumiko tried ways to swim through the water without making a splash or sound. She knew that she could swim better than anyone in the village. That thought made her less afraid of being caught when the thieves *did* come.

"I may have to give up tomorrow, Sumiko. My old bones like to sleep in our home," her grandmother said. "Now that the moon has left, we can't see very well."

Sumiko had been sleeping for only a short time when a

sound from the bay woke her. She heard splashing from
the direction of the oyster rafts. "Of course! They waited
for a dark night!" She woke her grandmother. Her grandmother left to awaken the people of the village. Then Sumiko went into the water.

Her feet kicked strongly. She used her arms under the
water, with her nose just out of the water.

Yes, she could see the shadows of two men by a canoe.
Her heart seemed to pound through the water. It was so
loud she thought the men would hear. They were too busy
diving with some kind of lights they wore attached to their
face masks.

Closing the new gate to the bay was the first part of her
plan. She and her grandmother had tied some of the bamboo poles together during the week they waited. They tied
them to the rocks on one side of the sea opening. The poles
could not be seen there at night. Sumiko swung them

around. She tied them to the rocks above and under the water. Then she swam straight for the canoe.

Splash! One of the men surfaced by the boat. Sumiko slipped under the water. When the man dived again, Sumiko quickly cut the canoe's anchor rope and raced to shore with the boat.

Grandmother put her arm around the girl's shaking shoulders. "The two men are trapped in the bay. They can't swim forever."

Finally the thieves swam to the small shore where the village people waited with lights. They tried to run, but the people gathered around them. There was no escape.

"We will take you to the island police in the morning," Mayor Yamada said. "Nothing like this has ever happened in our village. We want to be certain it won't happen again. To think a young girl showed the rest of us how to catch these men."

"You mean that girl trapped us?" said one of the men, frowning.

"Sumiko and her grandmother. We have the proof against you in the boat." The mayor turned to Sumiko and said, "I'm sorry you have lost more of your oysters."

"The ones in the boat are dead. We can still sell the pearls," Grandmother told him.

Sumiko took one of the oysters from the boat. She opened it with her knife. She felt for the hard, round lump. Even in the dark night the white gleam from the pearl flashed between her fingers as she lifted it from the shell.

"You have saved our treasure, Sumiko." Grandmother smiled. "Now let's go home. These old bones have had enough excitement to last for a long time!"

The Pearl:
A Gem of the Sea

Robin Jameson

Sumiko raises oysters for their pearls. Her work is more than just swimming in the sea. This article describes what the work is really like.

For thousands of years people have searched out the oyster. It is wanted not just as a food. People also want the beautiful gem that it makes—the pearl.

Oysters are shellfish. They live on the floors of the seas. They are found in many parts of the world.

How do people "catch" these oysters? In the Pacific Islands people dive for oysters. They have been diving for oysters for many years.

Without diving gear, people can dive no more than about 140 feet (42 meters). Without the gear, they can stay under the water no longer than two minutes at a time. These island people have found a way to speed their way down. They hold stones until they reach the bottom. Each person will spot an oyster, grab it, and rise to the surface to catch the side of the boat. Diving gear was invented many years ago. However, some of the people of Japan and the South Sea islands still dive for pearls without the aid of diving gear.

Where do people find oysters that make pearls? The best pearls are made by certain kinds of oysters. These oysters are not used for food. They live only in warm waters. They are often found in the waters off the coasts of Japan and the South Sea islands. They make their homes near coasts. In these places the waters are quiet and not very deep.

How does an oyster make a pearl? It first makes something called nacre. Nacre is also called mother-of-pearl. This matter is used to line the inside of the shell. Then it becomes hard. You may have seen this beautiful lining in an oyster shell. A grain of sand may enter the body of the oyster. The oyster then goes to work. It begins to make nacre. Coating after coating of this matter covers the grain of sand. After several years, the grain is well covered. A pearl has been formed.

What makes some pearls more valuable than others? When a valuable pearl is turned in the light, there is a play of colors, as in a rainbow. The colors may be pinks, purples, creams, and even shades of black. The black pearl is the most valuable of all. The shape of a pearl is also important. Round pearls bring the most money. However, button-shaped pearls are also valuable. These pearls are sometimes even called buttons. They are often used for earrings. A really fine pearl is not damaged or marked. Sometimes a pearl has only one tiny mark. The coating that has the mark can often be peeled by a trained person.

The sea holds many treasures. Many of these treasures were shaped by people. They are such things as gold and silver coins and art pieces. Many of these have gone down to the bottom of the sea in ships during terrible storms. The sea holds another kind of treasure, the pearl.

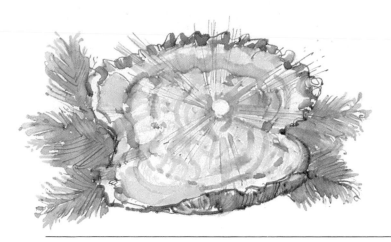

Answer these questions.

1. How did Sumiko at first try to prove that thieves were stealing oysters that belonged to her and her grandmother?

2. What did Mayor Yamada say might also have stolen the oysters?

3. Why was catching the thieves so important to Sumiko?

4. How did Sumiko and her grandmother catch the thieves?

5. How are pearls different from other gems, such as diamonds?

The Wheel on the School

Meindert DeJong

Shora is a small fishing village in Holland. Lina, the only girl in Shora, wishes there were storks there. If a stork builds a nest on one's roof, it is supposed to bring good luck. People in other villages put wagon wheels on their roofs so the storks will build nests on the wheels. The teacher has asked Lina and her classmates to think about why there are no storks in Shora. Lina is thinking very hard when she finds herself at the house of the oldest woman in the village.

"I know I'm a nosy old person," Grandmother Sibble III said. "There you stand again, staring. I've been watching you wandering. You go from the dike to the school and back again. You are just like a little lost sheep."

Lina laughed. It was a polite little laugh, though. "Oh, I'm not exactly wandering. I'm wondering."

"Oh," said the old lady, mystified. "Well, I guess wondering is always better than wandering. It makes more sense." She laughed.

They looked at each other. Lina thought how she had never talked much to Grandmother Sibble III. All she had ever done was to say a polite "hello" as she walked by. Now she did not know just what to say to her.

The old lady was still looking at her. "Is that why you have your shoe in your hand?" she said gently. "Because you were wondering so hard?"

In surprise Lina glanced down at her hand. She was holding the wooden shoe. She reddened a little. She hastily slipped it on her foot. What must Grandmother Sibble think? It was not that she was her real grandmother. She was just the grandmother of the whole village. She was the village's oldest old lady. It certainly must have looked silly to see Lina walking down the street on one shoe, carrying the other. No wonder Grandmother Sibble III had come out of the house!

"I . . ." Lina said. She tried to explain. "Oh, isn't it silly?" She fished in her mind for some way to explain that still made sense. None would come. Grandmother Sibble III wasn't standing there smiling in a superior, adult way. She just looked—well, puzzled and curious. Lina decided to tell her. "I guess it does look silly and odd. It somehow helps me think better to look into my shoe. Then I get to thinking really hard. I forget to put it back on again," she said.

"Why, yes," the old lady said. "Isn't it funny how odd little things like that help? Now I can think much better by sort of rocking myself. I've done it ever since I was a little girl like you." She carefully settled herself on the top step of her brick stoop. She looked as if she was settling herself for a good, long talk. "Now, of course, I've just got to know what it was you were thinking about so hard it made you forget your shoe." She chuckled her little old chuckle again. "If you don't tell me, I won't sleep all night from trying to guess."

They laughed together. Grandmother Sibble patted the

stoop next to her. "Why don't you come and sit down with me. Tell me about it."

Lina eagerly sat down—close, exactly where the old lady had patted. Old Grandmother Sibble was nice, she thought to herself. It was a nice surprise. She didn't talk to you as if you were a tiny tot, almost a baby, and miles of years away. She even understood silly things like looking into a wooden shoe. She understood it the way a girl friend—if you had a girl friend—would understand. A girl friend who also had silly tricks and secretly told you about them. Aloud Lina said, "I was thinking about storks, Grandmother Sibble. Why storks don't come and build their nests in Shora."

Grandmother Sibble looked thoughtful. "Well, that is a thing to think about all right. No wonder you had your shoe off. We here in Shora seem to always be without storks."

"I figured out why," Lina told the old lady proudly. "Our roofs are too sharp!"

"Well, yes . . . Yes, I guess so," the old lady said carefully. She sensed Lina's sharp excitement. "That could be taken

care of by putting a wagon wheel on the roof, couldn't it? The way they do in the villages?"

"Yes, I'd thought of that," Lina said. "My aunt in Nes has a wagon wheel on her roof. Storks nest on it every year."

"Ah, yes," the old lady said, "but doesn't your aunt's house have trees around it, too?"

"Yes, it has," Lina said. She looked in surprise at the old lady. Why, Grandmother Sibble must have been thinking about storks, too. It seemed surprising, the old, old lady thinking about storks. "I guess I never thought about trees. Well, just because there are no trees in Shora—so I didn't think about trees." Lina's voice faded away. Here was a whole new thing to think about.

"Would a stork think about trees?" the old lady wanted to know. "It seems to me a stork would think about trees. It seems to me that in order to figure out what a stork would want, we should try to think the way a stork would think."

Lina sat straight up. What a wonderful thing to say! Lina reached for her shoe. She eagerly looked at the old lady.

"You see, if I were a stork, even if I had my nest on a roof, I think I would still like to hide myself in a tree now and then. I would like to settle down in the shade and rest my long legs. Not be on the bare peak of a roof for everybody to see me all the time."

Lina pulled her feet up under her. She looked down puzzled at her wooden shoes. She really needed her wooden shoe right now. Her thoughts were racing.

"You see, years ago," Grandmother Sibble was explaining, "oh, years and years ago when I was the only girl in Shora, the way you are the only girl now, there were trees in Shora. There were also storks! The only trees in Shora grew on my grandmother's place. My grandmother was then the only grandmother of Shora. She was Grandmother Sibble I. Just like I am now Grandmother Sibble III and you would someday be Grandmother Sibble IV. That is if your mother had named you Sibble instead of Lina. I asked her to! Oh, I had no business asking. We're not even related. It just seems there should always be a Grandmother Sibble in Shora. That's beside the point.

"The point is, my grandmother's little house stood exactly where your school stands now but, oh, so different from your little school. Really different! My grandmother's house was roofed with reeds and storks like reeds. My grandmother's house was hidden in trees. Storks like trees. Weeping willow trees grew around the edge of a deep moat. It went all around my grandmother's house. In the shadowy water under the hanging willows, pickerel swam in the moat. Over the moat there was a little footbridge. It led right to my grandmother's door. In one of the willows there was always a stork nest. There was another nest on the low reed roof of my grandmother's house. As a little girl I used to stand on the footbridge. I

used to think that I could almost reach up to the low roof of the little house and touch the storks, so close they seemed."

"Oh, I didn't know. I never knew," Lina said.

Grandmother Sibble did not seem to hear. Her eyes were looking far, far back. She shook her head. "A storm came," she said, "as storms so often come to Shora. This was a real storm. The wind and waves roared up the dike for longer than a week. For a whole week the water pounded and the salt spray flew. The air was full of salt. You even tasted the salt on your bread in your house. When it was all done, there were only three willows left at Sibble's Corner. That is what they called my grandmother's house. That was because everybody met there on warm summer days to sit and talk and rest from work in the only shade in Shora. They wanted to talk and to lean their tired backs against the only trees. Then even those three leftover trees sickened and died. I guess their leaves had just taken in too much salt that long week of the storm.

"Later, Grandmother Sibble I died. They came and tore down her house. They chopped out the old rotted stumps of the willows. They filled the moat with dirt. There was nothing for years and years. Then they built your school on the same spot. The storks never came back."

Lina sat wide-eyed. She hugged her knees and stared straight ahead. She was drinking it in, dreaming it over—the things the old lady had said—dreaming the picture. It sounded like a faraway tale. Yet it had been! Grandmother Sibble III had seen it! She had thought as a little girl that she could reach up and touch the storks. It had been so real and so close. Right in Shora!

"I never knew. I never knew," Lina whispered to herself. "Even a little footbridge," she told herself. She hugged her knees.

Grandmother Sibble III roused herself. "So you see you must not think our sharp roofs are the whole story, must you?" she said softly. "We must think about other things, too. Like our having no trees, our storms, our salt spray. We must think about everything. To think it right, we must try to think the way a stork would think!"

Grandmother Sibble said "we"!

"Then have you been thinking about storks, too?" Lina asked in surprise.

"Ever since I was a little girl. Ever since then I've wanted them back. They're lucky and cozy and friendly and, well, just right. It's never seemed right again—the village without storks. Nobody ever did anything about it."

"Teacher says," Lina told the old lady softly, "that maybe if we wonder and wonder, then things will begin to happen."

"Is that what he said? Ah, but that is so right," the old lady said. "I'll sit on my stoop. You sit on yours. We'll think about storks. We'll think better on our own stoops. Often thinking gets lost in talking. Maybe your teacher is right. If we begin to think and wonder, somebody will begin to make things happen."

The old lady quietly let Lina wander off the stoop and to her own house. Lina had dreams in her eyes. She would not hear words anyway.

On her own stoop Lina looked back for the first time. There sat Grandmother Sibble III. She was rocking herself a little. The dream Lina was dreaming was not just about storks. At least it was not directly. Later she would think about storks. She would try to think the way a stork would think, as Grandmother Sibble had said. Now she thought about Grandmother Sibble. She had known storks, and when she was a little girl, had imagined she could reach up and almost touch the storks.

That was not the wonder either, not quite. The real wonder was that, just as the teacher had said, things *had* begun to happen. Begin to wonder why, the teacher had said. Maybe things will begin to happen. They had! For there sat Grandmother Sibble III on the stoop of her little house. Suddenly she had become important. She wasn't just an old person anymore, miles of years away. She was a friend. A friend, like another girl, who also wondered about storks.

Lina looked again at the old lady, sitting there on the stoop. She marveled. She sat feeling nice and warm about an old lady who had become a friend. Lina took one shoe off. She peered into it. Why, storks did bring good luck! The storks had made a friend for her.

About the Author

Meindert DeJong was born in the Netherlands. When he was eight years old, his family moved to the United States. Even though he grew up in America, the Netherlands were still important to him. Many of his stories, such as *The Wheel on the School,* are about the Dutch people and what their lives were like.

Answer these questions.

1. Why is Lina wondering about storks?

2. To whom does Lina think that Grandmother Sibble III is similar in the way that she understands things?

3. How was Grandmother Sibble III's life as a girl in Shora like Lina's life now?

4. Why is it so easy for Grandmother Sibble III to understand Lina's interest in storks?

5. What did Grandmother Sibble III like about storks that made her want them to come back to Shora?

6. How had storks brought good luck to Lina?

Reading in Health

Use your paper to complete the exercise below.

1. Look at the selection. What is the selection about?
2. Are there heads or subheads? What are they? What will each section be about?
3. Are charts, pictures, or diagrams used? What information do they give?
4. Are any words in boldface or italic type? List them.
5. Skim the material and make a list of words that are unfamiliar to you. Write the meanings of these words by using clues in the sentence or a dictionary.
6. Read the selection. List the important details.
7. In your own words write a paragraph that summarizes the information in the selection. If possible, use the words that you listed as unfamiliar or use synonyms for these words.

Posture

Posture, or how people stand and carry themselves, is important in keeping muscles and organs healthy.

How the Skeleton, Muscles, and Organs Work

When posture is incorrect, the skeleton and muscles must work harder to support the weight of the upper body. Muscles may become sore or even begin to grow incorrectly. The heart, lungs, and other organs will not work as well when a person's posture is bad.

Try this. Sit in a chair. Sit with shoulders slouched forward. Take a deep breath. Now sit up straight, shoulders back. Take a deep breath. In which position was it easier to breathe? Good posture makes the lungs' and other organs' work easier to do.

How You Look

Tall people look shorter when walking with *slumped,* or drooped, shoulders. Short people look taller when they stand up straight and walk with shoulders back and head up. Using good posture can make a person more *attractive,* or good-looking.

Sitting:
Sit with shoulders back.
Keep the back straight.

Walking:
shoulders back
back straight
head up

Poetry

Some people find everything just to their liking. Others know of things that they would like to change. These poems describe things some people like and wish for.

Rain Sizes

Rain comes in various sizes.
Some rain is as small as a mist.
It tickles your face with surprises,
And tingles as if you'd been kissed.

Some rain is the size of a sprinkle
And doesn't put out all the sun.
You can see the drops sparkle and twinkle,
And a rainbow comes out when it's done.

Some rain is as big as a nickle
And comes with a crash and a hiss.
It comes down too heavy to tickle.
It's more like a splash than a kiss.

When it rains the right size and you're wrapped in
Your rainclothes, it's fun out of doors.
But run home before you get trapped in
The big rain that rattles and roars.

John Ciardi

Travel

The railroad track is miles away,
 And the day is loud with voices speaking,
Yet there isn't a train goes by all day
 But I hear its whistle shrieking.

All night there isn't a train goes by
 Though the night is still for sleep and dreaming,
But I see its cinders red on the sky,
 And hear its engine steaming.

My heart is warm with the friends I make,
   And better friends I'll not be knowing,
Yet there isn't a train I wouldn't take,
   No matter where it's going.

Edna St. Vincent Millay

The Night Will Never Stay

The night will never stay,
The night will still go by,
Though with a million stars
You pin it to the sky;
Though you bind it with the blowing wind
And buckle it with the moon,
The night will slip away
Like a sorrow or a tune.

Eleanor Farjeon

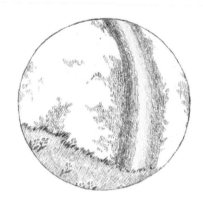

Answer these questions.

1. In the poem "Rain Sizes," what kinds of rain seem nice or fun?

2. What does the person in the poem by Edna St. Vincent Millay wish to do?

3. In the poem "The Night Will Never Stay," what two things will slip away in the same way that the night does?

Write on your own.

Think of something that you think would be a wonderful dream for someone to have as a goal. Write seven words that would describe this dream. Then write words that rhyme with these words. Use some of these words to write a four-line poem about the dream.

Einstein Anderson Makes Up for Lost Time

Seymour Simon

To Einstein Anderson science was more than just another class in school. It was the subject that interested him the most. However, he didn't just read about science and do experiments. This story tells how Einstein Anderson used what he knew about science.

Adam Anderson was Einstein's real name. Almost everyone called him Einstein, after one of the world's most famous scientists. Adam had been interested in science for as long as he could remember. He talked about science. He read about science. He experimented in science. He even solved puzzles by using science. For years even his teachers had called him Einstein.

Einstein Anderson was a twelve-year-old boy in the sixth grade. Sometimes his light-brown eyes had a strange look. You could tell that he was thinking about some question in science. Einstein was not always serious. He loved jokes of all kinds. He also liked to make puns. He liked the very bad puns the best.

The Icy Question

It was Saturday. Einstein wanted to sleep late. However, he had promised his friend Margaret that he would come over early. They were going to do some science experiments. Then they would eat lunch. After lunch they would go over to the school to play baseball.

Margaret was Einstein's friend and classmate. She was about as tall as Einstein. She was also good at sports. Science was her favorite subject, too. Einstein and Margaret were always working with microscopes. They enjoyed talking to each other about important science subjects. They also liked to talk about who was the best science pupil at Sparta Middle School.

Einstein soon arrived at Margaret's house. She was just feeding her fish. There were several different kinds. They were all at the top of the water. Each was grabbing for the food with a wide-open mouth.

Einstein looked at the fish for a minute. Then he turned to Margaret. "Do you know what one fish said to the other?" he said.

Margaret knew Einstein liked bad jokes. "What?" she said slowly.

"Keep your big mouth shut. Then you won't get caught."

"I shouldn't have asked," Margaret said. She shook back her red hair. "I've got to feed Orville and Wilbur. Next I have to take Nova for a walk. Then we can do some science experiments." Orville and Wilbur were Margaret's two cats. Nova was her dog. Margaret hadn't named her fish yet.

Margaret and Einstein took care of her pets. Then they went into the kitchen. The table had been cleared of dishes. On it were a knife, some wire, two brass weights, and a burner that made a small flame.

"I thought we'd do experiments with ice," said Margaret.

She opened the refrigerator. She took out a large block of ice. She placed the ice block on top of a dish rack in the sink.

"O.K., Einstein," she said. "Can you cut through this chunk of ice? However, you still have to leave one block of ice behind."

"What?" Einstein asked. "How can you cut through ice and not get more than one piece?"

"That's for me to know and you to find out," said Margaret. "Here's a hint. I hope you don't feel too much pressure in solving the puzzle."

Einstein went over to the ice. "If I heat the knife or a piece of the wire, it will cut through the ice," he said, thinking out loud.

"Then you'll have two pieces of ice left," said Margaret. "Do you give up?"

"Just a minute," Einstein said. He pushed back his glasses. Then he was quiet. His face lit up. "Give me a piece of wire and two bricks," he said. "I'll do it."

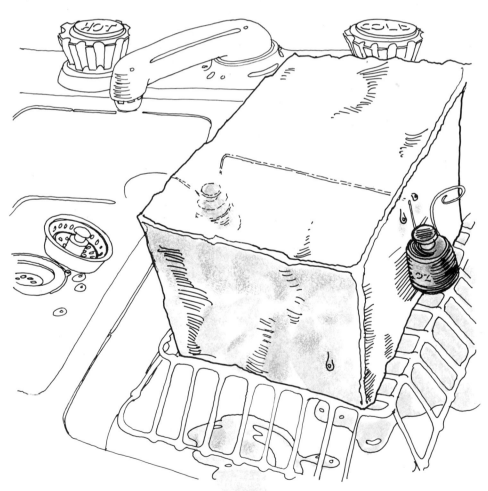

> *Can you solve the puzzle?* How can Einstein cut
> through a block of ice and yet leave one block
> behind?

Margaret's face fell. She rubbed her nose. "As soon as
you asked for two bricks, I knew you could do it," she said.
"Can you use these two brass weights instead of the
bricks?" she asked.

"Sure," said Einstein. "Let's work on it together."

Einstein and Margaret tied a brass weight to each end of
a piece of thin wire. Then they placed the weighted wire
on top of the ice. Slowly the wire began to pass through the
ice. Yet it left just one block behind.

"Your hint was a good one, Margaret," Einstein explained. "You said something about pressure. Pressure is
the key to the puzzle. The ice right under the wire melts.
That's because the pressure of the wire lowers the melting
point of the ice. The ice changes to water. The wire slips
down. However, the water freezes again as the wire passes
through and the pressure is gone."

"You're right as always," said Margaret. "Ice melting
under pressure is really the reason that you can skate on
ice. The ice melts beneath the weight of the skates. This
makes the skates move easily."

"I guess you could say that melting ice is just skid
stuff," said Einstein.

"I could," Margaret said. "I'd rather not."

The Impossible Trick

"Listen, children," Mrs. Taylor said. "The school fair is next Friday. There will be a used-book sale and a bake sale. There will be booth games, too. All the money made from the fair will be used to pay for our trip to Big Lake State Park later this month."

The class started to buzz. Everyone was looking forward to the fair. They were also excited about the trip to Big Lake. Mrs. Taylor, Einstein's teacher, waited a few minutes. Then she called on the class to quiet down.

"I want to have a group from this class decide on our class booth at this year's fair. Try to come up with something different. The class that earns the most money with its booth will go up to Big Lake a day early. Now who would like to be in the group? Hands, please."

Mrs. Taylor chose Pat Burns and his pal Herman. She also chose four others. She chose neither Einstein nor Margaret.

Later, during lunch recess, Margaret was talking to Einstein. "I wonder why Mrs. Taylor didn't choose either of us for that group," she said.

"Well, it's only fair that everyone gets a chance," Einstein said. "Maybe Mrs. Taylor thinks that scientists can't come up with an idea that's fun."

"I guess that's so," Margaret said. "You haven't even cracked one joke all day long. Maybe too much science makes you lose your sense of humor."

"Lose my sense of humor!" said Einstein. "Not very likely! I'm just like the scientist who first made spaghetti. I

can use my noodle to come up with an idea for a booth. It will be the hit of the fair.''

"Look," Margaret said. "Talk is cheap. Let's see you come up with a science booth that is fun. The group is going to report tomorrow on their idea for a booth. Why don't you come up with your own idea? It may be better than the group's idea. If so, I'm sure the class will go along with it.''

"I will," said Einstein. "Science *can* be fun. For now, let's go and eat an astronaut's favorite meal. Launch.''

The next day the group was giving their ideas about a booth for their class. They had chosen Pat to speak for the group because he had asked for the job. Pat said that he would do a good job.

"Here's what we want to do," Pat said to the class. "We're going to have a fortune-telling booth. We'll charge ten cents apiece to tell people's fortunes."

"But, Pat, what do you know about telling fortunes?" Mrs. Taylor asked.

"I could make them up," said Pat. "Who's going to know the difference?"

"I have an idea," said Einstein. "Suppose our class has The Booth of the Impossible Trick. You have to pay a dime to try it out. If you can do the trick, you win a dollar."

"Who's going to try to do an impossible trick?" asked Pat.

"That's the good part," said Einstein. "The trick sounds like it's easy to do. It's really impossible. We should get lots of people who'll try to win."

"How can a trick sound easy if it's really impossible?" asked Pat.

"Do you want to try it?" asked Einstein.

"Do I have to pay you a dime to try?" Pat asked slowly.

"No. This is for free," said Einstein. "All you have to do is bend over. Then touch your toes. You can't bend your knees."

"What!" said Pat. "That's easy. Anyone can do that."

"There is just one more thing, Pat," Einstein said. "You have to begin with your back and your feet against a wall. Your feet have to remain against the wall as you bend."

"So what?" said Pat. "I'm strong. I can touch my toes anywhere."

"Sorry," said Einstein. "It can't be done."

Can you solve the puzzle? How does Einstein
know that Pat cannot touch his toes without bending
his knees when his feet are against a wall?

Pat stood up against the front wall of the classroom. He
laughed. "Can you believe this?" he said. "Einstein is telling me that I can't touch my toes."

Pat started to bend over. He quickly lost his balance.
"Let me try that again," he said. Again Pat bent over. He
nearly fell down. He tried to do it several more times. Then
he said in disgust, "That's impossible. No one can do it."

"That's just what I told you, Pat," said Einstein. "The
trick sounds easy. It's really impossible."

"Einstein, that's really a great idea," Mrs. Taylor said. "I think it will make a great booth at the fair. Everyone will want to try it out. We can put the place to try out the trick behind a curtain. That way no one can see it's impossible to do."

Margaret raised her hand. "I agree with you, Mrs. Taylor," she said. "It really is a great idea. Science *can* be fun. Why is the trick impossible?"

"Would you please explain the trick, Einstein?" asked Mrs. Taylor.

"Sure," said Einstein. "It's all a matter of your center of gravity. That's the point where all your weight is concentrated. Your center of gravity is almost always right over your feet. If your center of gravity moves to a point outside your feet, then you fall over.

"Let's say that you bend over. You throw the upper part of your body forward. At the same time you move the lower part of your body back. Some weight moves forward. Some moves back. Your center of gravity stays the same. However, let's say you stand against a wall. The lower part of your body can't move back. All your weight moves forward. So you fall over when you try to touch your toes."

"That's wonderful, Einstein," Margaret said to him later.

"Thanks," said Einstein. "As Frankenstein said when he was hit by a bolt of lightning, 'Thanks, I needed that.'"

"You certainly haven't lost your sense of humor," Margaret said. "Too bad!"

Answer these questions.

1. What was Einstein and Margaret's hobby?

2. How did Einstein and Margaret spend their Saturday morning?

3. Are Einstein and Margaret often chosen to be in class groups? How do you know?

4. Why was the booth important to the class?

5. What was Einstein's idea for a booth?

6. What made Einstein's trick impossible?

Write on your own.

Imagine that you are in Einstein's class. Make a poster that advertises The Booth of the Impossible Trick. Include information such as what the booth looks like, how much it will cost, and why kids should go to the booth.

Taking Tests

Hints:

1. Before taking any kind of test it is important to understand and follow all of the directions. Carefully reading the directions will help explain how everything must be done. The directions tell where and how to show the answers and where to start. The teacher will answer questions about the test that are not understood after reading the directions. If the directions are misunderstood, the test may be completed in the wrong way. Answers that a person knows might then be marked incorrectly.

2. Some things make people feel better while taking a test.
   a. Wear comfortable clothes. People who wear clothes that are not comfortable may not be able to fully concentrate on the test.
   b. Make sure there is enough light. Misreading a question may cause an incorrect answer. Don't forget eyeglasses!
   c. Eat before taking any test. The brain needs food to work at its best. People don't want to think about a grumbling stomach during a test.

*****RELAX.
        ********THINK POSITIVELY.
              ******YOU CAN DO IT!

This exercise will help you practice test taking. Answer the questions and follow the directions below. Use your own paper.

1. Print your name at the top of the page. Write your last name first, then your first name, and then your middle name.

2. Look at the words in each row. Write the words that are the same.

   a. cake   fall   mother   cake   sit

   b. up   line   tree   line   car

   c. paper   jar   far   tea   far

3. Two words in each row have the same meaning. Write the words.

   a. dress   shirt   sleeve   hat   gown

   b. error   lie   mistake   truth   opinion

   c. large   little   green   unseen   small

4. One word in each row is different from the rest of the words.   Write that word on your paper.

   a. happy   happy   poppy   happy   happy

   b. sit   sit   sit   fit   sit

   c. lunch   munch   munch   munch   munch

5. In question number two, what do the directions tell you to do?

   a. write the words that are the same

   b. underline the words that are the same

   c. write the words that are opposites

   d. write the words that are spelled alike

6. Write the word that is not in alphabetical order.

   tracked   trail   trapped   tripped   trial

7. Write the answer that best completes the sentence.

   Many people love to _____ to the beach.

   a. stove   b. happy   c. paper   d. go

116

Albert Einstein

Ibi Lepscky   *translated by Ruth Parlé Craig*

Albert Einstein was one of the world's most brilliant scientists. He lived from 1879 until 1955, and he made many great contributions during his lifetime. However, when Einstein was young, people did not realize how smart he was. This biography tells about Einstein's life as a child.

About one hundred years ago, there lived a boy named Albert Einstein. Albert was a strange boy. He had trouble remembering some things. Also, he was not very neat. It was a difficult job for him to tie his shoes. However, he knew how to play the violin very well.

He did not like to play marbles or ball like others his own age. Instead, he enjoyed looking for hours and hours at the shape of a leaf. He liked playing with wooden blocks.

He did not like long sleeves. As soon as he could, he would use scissors to cut the sleeves. The sleeves would reach only to his elbows.

Einstein, a painting, by Mark English, courtesy of O'Grady Galleries, Chicago and Scottsdale.   117

He was not interested in the boys in his neighborhood who invited him to play war. He liked to chase the white chickens that scratched in the garden. He wanted to try to make friends with them.

Albert felt happy only with his little sister, Maja. He loved her very much. She looked just like him. They were as alike as two drops of water.

Sometimes Albert's cousins came to visit. They tried to get him to join in their games. "Albert is stupid," they said.

Albert did not listen to what they had to say. Maja and he watched some ants that were busy at work. He was a child different from others. His parents loved him very much. However, they were worried about him.

"Albert is a good boy," said his father one night. "But I would like it if he would study a little more and if he would show some interest in history and geography."

It was true. Albert did not like school. He did not like history and geography. He would not learn any lessons by heart. He was interested only in learning arithmetic.

"It would be nice if you could leave school, Albert," a teacher told him one day. "You don't listen. Your interest in class is poor. You set a bad example for the whole class."

Albert did not like sports. His classmates called him Albert the Incapable.

One day an older boy said, "Look in my eyes if you are brave enough."

Albert did not know that it was a dare. He was not listening carefully. His arms just hung at his sides. He had a faraway look on his face. He seemed lost in another world. He said softly, "Excuse me, but I'm not interested in your eyes."

The older boy did not understand Albert. He left, talking to himself.

"Oh," sighed his father. "Who will ever be able to understand what Albert has in his mind?"

Albert's mother loved him very much. She painted his picture on a little cup. Albert looked very neat in this picture. The little cup was always put on the family's fireplace.

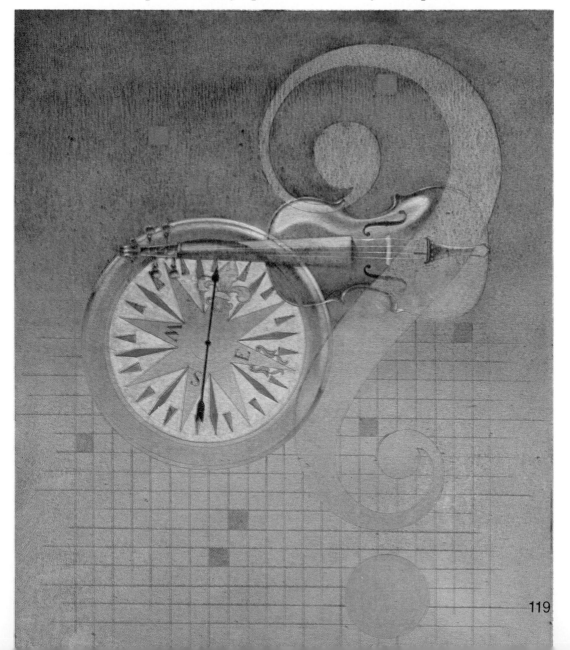

Albert's mother loved music very much. In the evenings she and Albert would play for the rest of the family. She would play the piano. Albert would play the violin.

One day Albert had a fever. He had to stay in bed for a few days. His father gave him a compass.

"Albert, you can pretend to be the captain of a ship," said his father. "You can decide the way to go with the compass."

Albert was not interested in his father's game. He wanted to know why the needle pointed to the big **N**. He wanted to know what magnetic fields were. He wanted to know where the poles of the earth could be found. He asked question after question. It seemed they would never end.

At last his father was tired. He said, "Because that's the way it is. That's all."

Later Albert's father thought back to all of the questions that Albert had asked. He was amazed that they were so good. They were exact and sharp. Suddenly he knew all about Albert. It filled him with pride, tenderness, and worry.

Albert was very different from other people. His faraway look was not because he could not remember things. His mind was just very busy. He was thinking of things no one had thought of before. He had the mind of a genius.

Albert's father was not wrong. When Albert grew up, he never lost his interest in the world and in science. He became a great scientist. He came up with new ideas that changed other people's ideas of what the universe was like. He discovered facts that had never been known before.

Albert had some of the greatest thoughts and ideas in the history of the world.

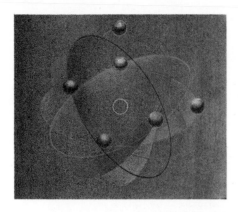

Answer these questions.

1. Who was the only person with whom Albert liked to play?

2. Why did the other students call Albert incapable?

3. Why would Albert study only certain subjects and play only certain games?

4. How did Albert's father at first feel about the questions that Albert asked about the compass?

5. Why did Albert's father change his mind about Albert's questions?

6. What did Albert's father learn about Albert?

Cabezón

Robert Cruz

Francisca and her mother look forward to a wonderful holiday trip by plane. Unfortunately, their plans change when a serious accident occurs. Francisca discovers that she has the courage and determination to help herself and her mother through their unexpected ordeal.

Mrs. Guterman was the fourth-grade teacher. She stood by the classroom door as her pupils poured out into the hall. Francisca Ribera was the last to leave.

"¡*Felices Pascuas*, Francisca!" Mrs. Guterman said with a big smile. Francisca's dark eyes sparkled.

"Happy holiday to you, too, Mrs. Guterman," Francisca answered. She zipped her coat against the cold December wind.

"Are you leaving town?" Mrs. Guterman asked.

"Yes, Mamá and I are flying to Albuquerque. We're going to visit my grandparents, Papá and Mamá Ribera."

"It's a long way from Lubbock to Albuquerque. The airline pilots know the way. I'm sure you'll have a good trip."

Francisca laughed. "Mamá rented a plane for the holidays. She's the best pilot in the world."

"I'm sure she is. Have a nice trip. I'll see you in two weeks."

"¡*Felices Pascuas!*" Francisca almost flew up the street. Her shiny black hair blew behind her as she ran. "Flying to Albuquerque . . . flying to Albuquerque," she sang in time to her feet on the sidewalk. She hardly slowed as she leaped up her front steps straight into the arms of her mother. "¡*Alto ahí!*" her mother said, laughing. "Stop! You're not flying yet." Her mother was a small, pretty woman. She was only a few inches taller than Francisca.

"Oh, excuse me, Mamá. I was afraid I'd be late."

"You're not late. You're right on time. The suitcases and packages are in the car. Are you ready?"

"Ready? Am I!" Francisca shouted. She climbed into the car and fastened her seat belt.

It was a thirty-minute drive to the airport. Holiday lights brightened the houses and stores along the streets. "Flying to Albuquerque . . . flying to Albuquerque," went round and round in Francisca's head.

"Here we are," her mother said. She parked the car next to a bright red and green airplane.

Francisca and her mother quickly loaded the Christmas packages and the suitcases into the plane. "In you go," Francisca's mother said. Francisca climbed in. Her mother closed the door tight after her and climbed in on the other side. "Is your seat belt tight?" Francisca's mother asked. She pushed the starter button.

"Yes, Mamá."

The starter whined. The cold engine coughed for a moment. Then it started. The propeller became a blur as it turned faster and faster.

Soon they were cleared for take-off. Slowly at first, then more and more rapidly, the little red and green plane rolled down the runway. The engine roared. The ground rushed by

Francisca's window. The airplane gave a little bump. Francisca knew they were in the air. Francisca and her mother were alone in the clear, blue winter sky. Far below, the trees were brown spots against the ground.

"What are you looking at, Francisca?"

"Oh, I'm just looking at the cars below on the highway. They look like tiny bugs," Francisca answered. Then she added with a grin, "I guess our airplane looks tiny to the people in the cars."

"Yes," Francisca's mother said, "that is true. However, you will have something more interesting to look at soon. I've been saving it as a surprise."

"A surprise? What is it, Mamá?"

"Do you remember where I was born? I've told you the story before—but not for a long time."

"In New Mexico?" Francisca answered.

"That's right. Where in New Mexico?"

Francisca thought for a moment as the plane flew through the air toward New Mexico.

"Oh, I remember now. You were born on a *rancho* near the mountain called Big Head. You lived there until Papá and Mamá Ribera moved to Albuquerque."

"Good! No one called it Big Head, though. Everyone used the Spanish name, Cabezón. The mountain does look like a giant's head. It frightened me when I was a little girl. The place where I was born is gone now. The town of Cabezón is at the foot of the mountain. It is just a ghost town on the river."

Francisca's eyes shone with excitement. "That's my surprise! We are going to Cabezón, where you were born!"

Francisca's mother smiled. "I'm afraid ghost towns have

no airports. We are going to fly over the giant's head, Cabezón, though. You will be able to see the town and the river."

On and on the little airplane flew. For a while Francisca stayed awake. Halfway to Albuquerque, the smooth hum of the motor and the warm air inside the plane made her eyelids heavy. Soon she was asleep. Her mother leaned over. She smoothed Francisca's hair and smiled. "You are a good daughter, Francisca, even if you are asleep and cannot hear me tell you so."

Francisca's mother hummed happily to herself as she flew the little plane into New Mexico. Finally she gave Francisca's arm a gentle tug to awaken her. "Francisca, look below."

Francisca rubbed her eyes. She yawned and looked out the window. Beneath the plane a huge city was spread like a brightly colored quilt. "What city is that?"

"That is Albuquerque, the home of your grandparents."

Francisca groaned, "Oh, no! We are here. I missed Cabezón. Why didn't you wake me sooner?"

"You didn't miss Cabezón. It is on the other side of Albuquerque. We will fly over the Cabezón. Then we'll fly back to Albuquerque."

"Oh," Francisca said quietly. "I think I'll stay awake now."

"Look out the window, Francisca. Do you see that highway? It looks like a silver ribbon."

"Yes," Francisca answered.

"We will follow that highway for a short way. Then we will turn west. Then you see if you can find Cabezón, the giant's head."

In a moment Francisca felt the plane bank sharply to the left. She looked through the window at the ground below. There were few trees, only scrubby brush. The brown land was cut with *arroyos*. From her seat in the airplane Francisca could see that they all finally ran into a dry riverbed. "Is that the river, Mamá?"

"Yes, and before long you should see Cabezón."

"It should be called dry river," Francisca said half to herself.

"I have seen a sudden storm fill the *arroyos* with rushing water. It flows into the river until the water nearly spills over its banks," Francisca's mother said.

"Look!" Francisca shouted. "Look over there! Cabezón! It looks just like . . ."

Before she could finish, the airplane shook.

"Mamá, what?"

Francisca's mother worked at the controls of the airplane. The motor coughed once. Then it died. For a moment the only sound was the whistling of the wind outside the plane. "Mayday! Mayday! This is November one eight niner seven Oscar." She stopped. The radio was as dead as the engine. Francisca's mother spoke quietly. She fought to hold the plane level. "Francisca, tighten your seat belt as much as you can. Cover your face with your arms. We must land the plane."

Francisca's eyes grew wide with fear. "There is no place to . . . !"

"Relax, my daughter," Francisca's mother said quietly. "We will be safely on the ground in a moment. Now do as I say."

For a second Francisca stared at the rough ground below. It was bare and unfriendly and frightening. The last thing Francisca saw before she covered her face was Cabezón, the giant's head. It was standing in the distance like an ugly guard.

Time seemed to stop for Francisca. She could hear only the wind. Then with a hard jolt they were on the ground. Brush whipped against the bottom of the plane as it bounced across the rough, rocky earth. Suddenly Francisca felt as if the ground had been jerked from beneath the plane. Almost at once there was a terrible, grinding crash. The plane had nosed into the side of an *arroyo*. Francisca was thrown hard against her seat belt. She felt as if she would never breathe again.

The plane rested on its nose deep in the brushy *arroyo*. One wing hung down like the wing of an injured bird.

"Francisca . . . Francisca, can you hear me? Are you hurt?" Francisca's mother's voice shook a little.

Francisca fought for breath. Finally she was able to speak. "I . . . I think I'm OK," she said weakly.

Her mother sighed with relief. Then she groaned softly. Francisca turned quickly in her seat. "You're hurt, Mamá!" She could see the pain in her mother's eyes. "Where are you hurt?"

"My leg, Francisca. I think my leg is broken."

"Mamá, what can we do? We must be miles from town." Francisca could feel tears in her eyes. Her throat felt as if a large stone were stuck in it. She swallowed. "How can we call for help?"

"The radio is out. We will just have to wait for someone to find us."

Francisca felt a tear run down her cheek. *No*, she thought, *I must be brave. I am not hurt. I must be brave.* She felt another tear. She turned toward the window.

She could not see beyond the edge of the deep, wide *arroyo* that the plane had crashed into. Around the plane, twisted bushes grew in bunches in the dry, brown soil.

"Francisca . . ." her mother called softly.

Francisca quickly rubbed her eyes. She turned to face her mother.

"Francisca, listen carefully. My leg is broken. I must depend on you." Her mother's voice was calm. Her face was pale. "I am sure we will not be missed before morning. So we must spend the night here."

"Can't we stay in the plane?" Francisca asked.

"No," her mother answered, "you should never stay in an *arroyo*. It is dry now. If it should rain, the *arroyo* would fill with water rushing down to the river. We must get out of the plane. We will have to make a splint to hold my leg. That is

why I must depend on you. Climb out of the plane. Find two straight branches. While you are gone, I will get out of the airplane."

Francisca turned the handle on the door and pushed. She could not move it. It was stuck tight from the crash. She unfastened her seat belt. Then she turned half around in her seat. Placing both feet against the door, she pushed hard. Still the door did not move. She gritted her teeth and pulled her legs back. She kicked as hard as she could. With a crack, the door popped open. Francisca dropped to the ground.

The sides of the *arroyo* were steep. Quickly she glanced around. There was nothing for a splint near the plane. "I must get out of this *arroyo*," she said to herself.

The rough ground made climbing hard. Three times she tripped. She fell to her hands and knees to keep from falling backward. Using the scrubby brush to pull herself along, she

called. "Mamá!" There was only the whistling of the cold
wind. Francisca scrambled down into the *arroyo*. She ignored
the brush that tore at her face and body. Her mother lay on the
ground next to the plane. "Mamá!" she repeated. She knelt
next to her mother.

"Francisca . . . Francisca, I must have fainted. Did you find
some sticks?"

"Yes, Mamá. Are you all right?"

"I will be. I am sure. We must get out of here."

Francisca fought her way up out of the *arroyo* again. She
threw the boards to the bottom of the *arroyo*. Then she
climbed back down to her mother.

Her mother placed a board on each side of her hurt leg.
Then she tore wide bands of cloth from the lining of her coat.
"Francisca, you will have to help me. Wrap the cloth tightly
around the boards. My leg must be held still between them. It
cannot move."

Francisca began at her mother's ankle. Once her mother groaned softly. "Is that too tight, Mamá?" she asked.

"No . . . no, the leg is just sore. Go on. It must be tight."

At last Francisca finished. "You still cannot walk on it," Francisca said. "How can you climb up the side of the *arroyo*?"

"I am afraid I must depend on you again, my daughter. You must take the place of my bad leg. Do you think you can?"

Before Francisca could answer, thunder rumbled from the direction of Cabezón. "I must, Mamá. I must," Francisca answered.

"Can you do one more thing, Francisca? We must have something to eat and something to drink. We must have a fire

Vocabulary Review

On your paper write **a, b, c,** or **d** to show the item that best completes the sentence.

1. Paddling a canoe is paddling a kind of _____.
   - a. boot
   - b. water
   - c. boat
   - d. sport

2. Something that was hastily done was done _____.
   - a. quietly
   - b. quickly
   - c. carefully
   - d. slowly

3. A shrieking whistle may hurt ears with its _____.
   - a. playing
   - b. screaming
   - c. signaling
   - d. screening

4. When people are unhappy, they feel sorrow, or _____.
   - a. joy
   - b. hate
   - c. sadness
   - d. sickness

5. An impossible task may be so hard that it is _____.
   - a. unworkable
   - b. unexpected
   - c. uncombed
   - d. unworried

6. A person who can't do something is incapable, or _____.
   - a. beautiful
   - b. unarmed
   - c. wasteful
   - d. unable

7. The deserted house was empty and _____.
   - a. large
   - b. abandoned
   - c. funny
   - d. beautiful

144

Books to Read

Aldis, Dorothy   *Nothing is Impossible: The Story of Beatrix Potter*

Hunca Munca and Peter Rabbit were not only characters in Beatrix Potter's books but also the names of pets that she had at different times. This book tells the story of Beatrix Potter's life.

Clymer, Eleanor   *A Search for Two Bad Mice*

Barbara, Sarah, and their parents go to England on vacation. Sarah misses their cat, Leo, and is not happy until they visit Beatrix Potter's home. Sarah talks Barbara into a search for Hunca Munca.

Hughes, Dean   *Honestly, Myron*

After hearing the story of Abraham Lincoln's greatness, Myron decides that he is going to be completely honest in everything that he does. This story tells what happens when he keeps his promise.

Lawson, Robert   *Ben and Me*

Benjamin Franklin was a leader of the American Revolution and an inventor. Robert Lawson invented Amos, a mouse who lived in Ben's fur hat. Amos tells Ben's story and takes the credit for Ben's inventions.

Simon, Seymour   *Einstein Anderson Makes Up for Lost Time*

Adam Anderson is so interested in science that he is known as Einstein. These stories tell the ways in which he uses science in his everyday life.

INSIGHTS

Who has seen the wind?
  Neither you nor I:
But when the trees bow down their heads,
  The wind is passing by.

                    Christina Rossetti

Sound of Sunshine, Sound of Rain

Florence Parry Heide

    Often people who can see have difficulty imagining what the world is like to a blind person. The boy who tells this story is blind. His world is full of sounds and different things to feel. Read about his world. You may get a different view of your own world.

It must be morning, for I hear the morning voices. I have been dreaming of a sound that whispers *Follow me, Follow me,* but not in words. I follow the sound up and up until I feel I am floating in the air.

Now I am awake, and I listen to the voices.

My mother's voice is warm and soft as a pillow.

My sister's voice is little and sharp and high, like needles flying in the air.

I do not listen to the words but to the sound. Low, high, low, high, soft, hard, soft, hard, and then the sounds come together at the same time and make a new sound. And with it all, the sharp sounds of my sister's heels put holes in what I hear.

Then I hear the slamming of kitchen drawers and the banging of pans and there is no more talking.

My bed is in the living room. I reach out to feel whether my mother has laid my clothes on the chair beside my bed. They are there, and I feel the smoothness and the roughness of them.

I reach under the chair to find which shoes my mother has put there. They are my outside shoes, not my slippers, so today must be a warm day. Maybe I can go to the park. I tap my good luck song on the wall beside my bed.

I put my feet on the floor and feel the cool wood and curl my toes against it.

Then it is four steps to the table, then around the table, touching the chairs, and then seven steps to the window. I put my cheek against the window, and I can feel the warm sun. Now I am sure I can go to the park, if my sister has time to take me on her way to class.

I take my clothes into the bathroom, and I wash and dress there. Hot water, cold water, soapy water, plain water, loud water, still water. Then I make sure I have turned the faucets tight. I make sure I have buttoned all of my buttons the right way, or my sister will be cross, and maybe not have time to take me to the park.

I tap my good luck song against the door before I open it.

When I open the door, I hear the voices again. My sister's voice is like scissors cutting away at my mother's voice.

I sit at the table, and my mother gives me my breakfast. I breathe on the hot chocolate so I can feel it on my face coming back warm. I drink just a little at a time so I can keep holding the warm cup.

"Eat while it's hot," says my sister to me, loud.

"Does he have to be so slow?" says my sister to my mother in her quiet voice. My sister thinks because I cannot see that maybe I cannot hear very well, and she talks loud to me, and soft when she does not want me to hear, but I hear.

"You spilled," says my sister, loud.

"I can't be late," she says in her quiet voice to my mother. "Everybody's always late but me, and I won't be late."

After breakfast I go over to the window again, and when I put my cheek against the glass it is warmer than before, so today will be a good day. I tap my good luck song against the window.

My sister says she will take me to the park on her way to class. She gives me my jacket and tells me to wait for her outside on the steps.

I go down the outside steps. There are seven steps. Seven is my most magic number. Seven up, seven down, seven up, seven down. I go up and down, waiting for my sister.

My sister comes out. She takes my hand. She walks very fast, but I can still count the steps to the park, and I can still remember the turns. Someday I can go there by myself. I listen to the street noises and try to sort them out.

My sister's hand is not soft. I can feel her nails, little and sharp, like her voice, and I listen to her heels making holes in all the other sounds.

The park seems a long way off.

When we get to the park we go first to the bench. She waits to make sure I remember my way in the park.

Fourteen steps to the bubbler. Around the bubbler, twenty steps to the curb.

I go back to the bench. I try to hurry so my sister won't have to wait long and be cross. Now seventeen steps to the phone booth, four benches on the way, and I touch them all. Then I come back to the bench.

My sister puts money in my pocket so I can telephone.

She talks to me and to herself.

"Filthy park," she says, and it is as if she were stepping on the words. "No grass. Trees in cages. Since when do benches and old newspapers make a park?" She pulls my jacket to straighten it.

Now she is gone and I have my morning in the sun.

I try each bench, but mine is still the best one.

I go to the bubbler and press my mouth against the water and feel it on my tongue, soft and warm. I put my finger on the place where the water comes out and walk around and around the bubbler, and then I try to find my bench. It is one of my games. I have many games.

I walk over to the telephone booth, touching the four benches on the way. I stand inside the booth. I feel to see whether there is any money in the telephone, but there is none. My sister says I should always check the telephone for money, but I have never found any.

I practice dialing our number so I will be sure I have it right. Then I put my dime in and call. I let it ring two times and then I hang up and get my dime back. My sister says that way my mother will know I am all right.

I blow on the glass, and it blows back to me. I tap my good luck song on it and go back to my bench.

I play one of my games. I listen to every sound and think if that sound would be able to do something to me, what it would do. Some sounds would scratch me; some would pinch me; some would push me. Some would carry me, some would crush me, and some would rock me.

I am sitting on my bench tapping my good luck song with my shoes when I hear the bells of an ice-cream truck. I feel the money in my pocket. I have the dime, and I also have a bigger one. I know I have enough for an ice-cream bar.

I walk out to the curb, touching the cages around the trees. I wait until the bells sound near, and I wave.

He stops. He is near enough for me to touch his cart. I hold out my money.

Now I feel him seeing me, but he does not take my money.

"Here," I say, but he does not take the money from me.

"Guess what?" he says, and his voice is soft and kind as fur. "Every tenth kid wins a free ice-cream bar, and you're the lucky one today."

I can feel him getting off his cart and going around to open the place where he keeps his ice-cream bars. I can feel him putting one near my hand, and I take it.

I start back to my bench.

"Are you going to be okay by yourself now?" the ice-cream man calls, so I know he is seeing me.

I sit on the bench. I listen for the sound of his cart

starting up, and his bells ringing, but I can only hear the other sounds, the regular ones.

Then I hear him walking over to my bench.

I am sorry, because I only want to feel the ice cream and see how long I can make it last. I do not want anyone to sit with me now. I am afraid I will spill it, and he will see me.

He starts to talk, and his voice is soft as a sweater.

His name is Abram. He tells me about the park.

My sister says the trees are in cages because if they weren't in cages, they wouldn't stay in such a terrible park, they'd just get up and go somewhere pretty.

Abram says the trees are in cages to keep them safe so they can grow to be big and tall. "Like sides on a crib

for a baby, keeping the baby from falling and getting hurt," says Abram.

My sister says the park is ugly and dirty.

Abram says there are a few little bits of paper, and a couple of cans and some bottles, but he says he can squint up his eyes and all those things lying around shine like flowers. Abram says you see what you want to see.

My sister says that the park is just for poor folks and that no one would ever come here if they had a chance to go anywhere else.

Abram says the park is just for lucky people, like him and me. He says the people who come to this park can see things inside themselves, instead of just what their eyes tell them.

After a while Abram goes away. He says he will come back and look for me tomorrow. I hear his ice-cream bells go farther and farther away until I do not hear them anymore.

While I am waiting for my sister to come for me, I fall asleep on the bench.

I have a good dream. I dream that Abram lifts me so I can touch the leaves of a tree. All the leaves are songs, and they fall around me and cover me. I am warm and soft under the songs.

My sister shakes me awake. "You'll catch cold lying here," she says.

The next day while I am sitting on my bench, I hear the ice-cream bells, and I walk out to the curb, touching the cages of the trees as I go. Abram gives me an ice-cream bar, and we walk together back to the bench. I do not have to touch the cages because I am with him.

After I finish my ice-cream bar, Abram gives me some paper clips so I can feel them in my pocket. He shows me how I can twist them to make little shapes.

After he leaves, I feel them. There are seven paper clips.

That night I dream that someone is gathering in a big net everything in the world that makes a sound, and I am tumbled in the net and my sister shakes me awake.

"Stop thrashing around," she says. "You're all tangled up in the blanket."

The next day Abram brings me a balloon.

I can feel it round and tight. It tugs at the string.

Abram says some balloons are filled with something special that makes them want to fly away, up to the sun, and this balloon is filled with that something special.

He says some people are filled with something special that makes them pull and tug, too, trying to get up and away from where they are.

His voice is like a kitten curled on my shoulder.

He tells me my balloon is red, and then he tells me about colors.

He says colors are just like sounds. Some colors are loud, and some colors are soft, and some are big and some are little, and some are sharp and some are tender, just like sounds, just like music.

What is the best color, I wonder?

He says all colors are the same, as far as that goes.

There isn't a best color, says Abram. There isn't a good color or a bad color.

Colors are just on the outside. They aren't important at all. They're just covers for things, like a blanket.

Color doesn't mean a thing, says Abram.

When my sister comes, she asks me where I got my balloon.

I tell her about my friend.

I hold onto the string of my balloon while we walk.

We stop at a store. When we go in, I hold my balloon against me so it won't get hurt.

The store feels crowded. I hear a lady's voice. It sounds as if she was squeezing it out of her like the last bit of toothpaste in a tube.

The lady's voice says, "Better wait on this black lady first."

My sister takes my hand and pulls me away. I hold my balloon tight.

"So we're black," says my sister to me as she pulls me along. "So what else is new? I've heard it a million times. I guess I heard it before I was even born."

"Abram says color don't mean a thing," I say.

My sister drags me along. I can tell by her hand that she's mad.

"What does he know? Is he black, your friend?" she asks.

"I don't know," I say.

"You don't even know if your friend is black or not," says my sister. "I wish everyone in the whole world was blind!" she cries.

When we get home, I tie the string of my balloon to my chair.

I have a bad dream in the night. I dream that my ears are sucking in every sound in the world, so many sounds I cannot breathe. I am choking with the sounds that are pulled into me, and I have to keep coughing the sounds away as they come in or I will smother.

"Here's some stuff for your cold," says my sister.

When I am awake again, I cannot tell if it is morning. I hear noises, but they are not the morning noises. My sister has her quiet voice, and I do not hear the little hard sounds of her heels making holes in the morning.

She is wearing slippers. She tells my mother she is not going to go to class today.

There is no hurry about today. I reach for my balloon. The string lies on the chair, and I find the balloon on the floor, small and soft and limp. It does not float. It lies in my hand, tired and sad.

I lie there and listen to the sound of slippers on the kitchen floor.

I tap my good luck song against the wall over and over, but I hear the rain and know I will not go to the park today.

Tomorrow it will be a nice day. Tomorrow my sister
will feel better, and I will go to the park and find
Abram. He will make my balloon as good as new.

Now I walk over to the window and lean my head
against it.

The rain taps its song to me against the glass, and I
tap back.

Answer these questions.

1. Why does the boy want it to be warm outside?

2. How is the boy able to get around his house and the park easily?

3. Who is Abram? What did Abram mean when he said, "you see what you want to see"?

4. What did Abram tell the boy about colors?

5. How does the boy feel about his sister? How do you know?

The Arrow and the Song

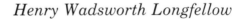

I shot an arrow into the air,
It fell to earth, I knew not where;
For so swiftly it flew, the sight
Could not follow it in its flight.

I breathed a song into the air,
It fell to earth, I knew not where;
For, who has sight so keen and strong
That it can follow the flight of song?

Long, long afterward, in an oak
I found the arrow, still unbroke;
And the song, from beginning to end,
I found again in the heart of a friend.

Henry Wadsworth Longfellow

Miss Pickerell Goes to Mars

Ellen MacGregor

Miss Pickerell spends a month each year visiting her seven nieces and nephews. This year she finds that a spaceship has been built in her pasture while she has been away. When she enters the ship, the people mistake her for Mr. Haggerty, the last member of the crew. They blast off with Miss Pickerell instead of Mr. Haggerty. Miss Pickerell finds herself on the way to Mars. All of the new things she experiences, such as weightlessness, make her want to return home. After all, she has left behind a sick cow that she must care for. However, as the trip continues, she finds her feelings about the trip are changing.

"This is it!" Miss Pickerell heard someone shout. "We're here! We've landed."

With great effort, Miss Pickerell managed to turn her heavy head in the direction of the men.

Wilbur and Mr. Killian were standing upright, close together, clapping each other on the back. The captain stood to one side. Each man in turn took his hand and shook it solemnly and respectfully.

Miss Pickerell tried to sit up. She found that she couldn't. She seemed to weigh tons. She couldn't move her heavy body.

"Help!" she called. "I can't move! I'm paralyzed!"

"No, you aren't, Miss Pickerell," Wilbur said. He walked toward her with tired-seeming steps. "It just seems that way because we've been without gravity for so long. You'll soon get used to it. You'll feel wonderful. You'll feel a lot lighter here on Mars than you did on Earth."

Wilbur was right. Very soon, Miss Pickerell was able to sit up. She stepped down to the floor of the room. It was a strange sensation to be using her leg muscles again after such a long time of floating through the air.

"Well," she said to the captain. He was looking across the room at her. "What are we waiting for? Let's open the door and go out."

The captain walked slowly toward her.

He said, "Do you see those bulky suits with the clear helmets that the men are putting on? Those are pressure suits. Each person who leaves the ship must wear one, in order to remain alive."

"I don't mind," Miss Pickerell said. "I'll wear Mr. Haggerty's suit. Which one is his?"

"Miss Pickerell—"

"Couldn't she come, Captain?" Wilbur asked. "I'll watch out for her."

"That's beside the point. I cannot take the responsibility of letting you leave the ship. You are not trained for this kind of thing. However, you may listen to our conversation on the radios. All of our suits have radios. You can hear everything that we say to each other. If you get too lonely, you may speak to us."

She watched the men getting ready to leave the ship. Each put on a bulky-looking suit and a clear helmet. Inside each helmet was a small microphone just in front of the person's mouth.

Wilbur kept his helmet off till the last. That way he could explain things to Miss Pickerell.

He told her about the atmospheric pressure of Mars. It was much less than that of the earth. He explained that the suits must maintain the same pressure as that of the earth. He told her how the atmosphere of Mars did not have enough oxygen. He showed her the air tanks. Each person carried one of these tanks in a large pocket on the back of the suit. Wilbur showed Miss Pickerell how the tank was hooked up to the suit. Also he explained the temperature of Mars. During most of the day and all of the night, it would be far too cold for comfort or safety. That was why the suits were heated.

Then he took her to the door of the ship and explained the pressure lock to her. Mr. Killian was just entering the lock. Miss Pickerell wouldn't have known

it was Mr. Killian if he hadn't turned around so that she could see his face through the clear front of the helmet. In the bulky brown suits, the men looked just alike.

"See, Miss Pickerell," Wilbur said. "He opens the inside door of the lock and goes in. He closes the door and adjusts the pressure valve. The outside door of the lock won't open until the pressure inside the lock is the same as that outside. Do you understand, Miss Pickerell?"

Miss Pickerell said, "It's nice of you to try to explain it to me, Wilbur."

The last person to leave the ship, the last person to

go through the lock, was the captain. "We won't be gone long, Miss Pickerell," he said. He was talking to her by radio because he had already fastened his helmet. It sounded strange to hear his voice coming out of the radio in the captain's cabin behind Miss Pickerell. After all, she could see his lips moving as he stood directly in front of her.

"We'll be back within half an hour," the captain said. "Half an hour at the most." Then he stepped into the lock. He closed the inside door.

Miss Pickerell was left alone.

Almost immediately, Miss Pickerell heard the voice of the captain coming from the radio in his cabin.

"Miss Pickerell," he said. "Did I leave my watch in there?"

Miss Pickerell hurried into the captain's cabin. The watch was on a bench. She noticed that it was just half past twelve.

"Yes, Captain," she said. She stooped to speak into the radio on a bench in front of the captain's chair. "I'll bring it to you. I'll put on Mr. Haggerty's suit. Then I'll bring it right out."

"Miss Pickerell," the captain said, "you are to remain on the ship. Those are my orders. I just wanted to be sure that my watch was there. Do not leave the ship under any circumstances."

Miss Pickerell did not answer.

She went back and sat down in the captain's chair. From time to time she heard the men speaking into the radio. Sometimes they talked to her. Then she would answer them. "Don't tell me what it's like," she said. "I want to see for myself. That is, when the captain lets me go out."

"I'll bring you a souvenir, Miss Pickerell." It was Wilbur's voice. "How would you like a rock?"

"A rock!" Miss Pickerell exclaimed. "Are there rocks right out there?"

"All kinds," Wilbur said. "Red, mostly. They're very pretty. I'll bring you one."

Now Miss Pickerell was twice as eager to get outside. Red rocks from Mars would make a wonderful addition to her rock collection at home.

"Come back, Wilbur." This was the captain's voice. "You're getting too far away from us."

"All right," Wilbur said. "I'm just getting a red rock for Miss Pickerell."

"Miss Pickerell. What time is it?" the captain asked.

Miss Pickerell looked at the captain's watch. "It's a quarter to one," she said.

"All right, men," the captain said. "Everybody turn around. Go back to the ship. We'll run out of air if we stay away any longer."

Miss Pickerell heard Wilbur's voice. "Captain, something's happened. I'm stuck. My foot is caught between two big rocks. Help me, Captain."

Miss Pickerell listened for the captain's answer. "Here we come, Miss Pickerell," was all he said.

"Captain!" Miss Pickerell shrieked. Something must have happened to his radio. He must not have heard Wilbur's call.

Miss Pickerell remembered that once before this had happened. On the very first day of the flight, Wilbur had tried to report her from the pasture gate to the spaceship. The radio had been out of order at first.

Again she heard Wilbur's voice. "Please, Captain. I need help."

"What is it, Miss Pickerell?" said the captain's voice. "Is anything the mat—" There was a sharp click and then silence. The radio had gone dead. Miss Pickerell shouted into the radio. There was no answer from the captain, or from Wilbur, or from Mr. Killian.

For seconds, Miss Pickerell sat there, stiff with horror. Unless the captain turned around, he would never know that Wilbur was not right behind him. Wilbur would run out of air. . . .

"Wilbur," Miss Pickerell said, just in case he was still able to hear her voice. "Don't be frightened! I'm coming. I'm coming to help you."

She dashed to where they had left Mr. Haggerty's suit. She picked it up. It was heavy. She struggled into

it, one foot at a time. She took an air tank and put it into the big loose pocket on the back of the suit. She lifted the helmet over her head and fastened it. This was hard to do because of the thick gloves that sealed the ends of her sleeves.

Last of all, Miss Pickerell hooked up the air tank to its opening in the suit, the way Wilbur had showed her. She hurried to the lock. Just before she entered it, she went back and took another air tank in her arms. This would be for Wilbur in case he ran out of air before they could free his foot.

Inside the lock, she closed the inside door. She remembered Wilbur had said something about adjusting the pressure valve. In the wall of the lock was a small handle. Miss Pickerell turned this. There was a hoarse sucking sound. In a few moments, Miss Pickerell was able to open the outside door.

She almost fainted when she saw how high above the ground she was. There was a thin ladder leading down to the red rocky waste below. She would have to climb down this, wearing the suit and carrying the extra tank of air for Wilbur.

Miss Pickerell did not wait. Somehow, slipping and hanging on at each rung, and keeping her eyes tightly closed, she fought against her dizziness. Somehow, she was able to get to the ground. She opened her eyes.

Far away, she could see Wilbur. He would wave his arms in the air. Then he would stoop down to try to free his trapped foot.

Between Wilbur and the spaceship, and coming toward her, Miss Pickerell saw the other men. Neither one had missed Wilbur. Each man must have thought Wilbur was following behind.

Clutching the extra air tank, Miss Pickerell lumbered toward the men. It was hard to walk in the heavy suit. The ground was rough and rocky. Now and then the wind blew thick clouds of red dust across the front of her helmet.

She waved and pointed, trying to make the men
turn around and look back. But this only made them
walk faster. As they neared each other, Miss Pickerell
could see the face of the captain in the lead. He took
long, angry steps. His blue eyes were blazing. His lips,
inside the clear helmet, were moving. Although Miss
Pickerell could not tell what he was saying, she knew
he must be angry at her for leaving the ship.

"Captain!" she shouted. "Captain!" If only the radio
would work.

The captain had almost reached her now. He tried to
take hold of her arm, but Miss Pickerell pulled away.
She said the word "Wilbur" over and over. She
stretched her lips wide each time, hoping that the captain would understand.

Then she suddenly took the captain by the sleeve of his suit and partly turned him around. She pointed again. This time the captain saw.

The captain looked for only a second. Very quickly he unhooked his air tank and replaced it with the one Miss Pickerell was wearing. After he had hooked up the tank he had been wearing to her suit, he took the extra tank from her arms. He hurried out across the rocks toward Wilbur.

Miss Pickerell started to follow. A gentle pull restrained her. It was Mr. Killian. Miss Pickerell turned back toward the ship. She understood now. The captain's tank of air was not full enough to take her far. She would have to go back and wait inside the ship until the captain and Wilbur returned.

Mr. Killian pointed out that she was to climb the ladder and enter the lock. From the top of the ladder, Miss Pickerell took one look back. She had the satisfaction of seeing that the captain had reached Wilbur. With one powerful tug, he freed Wilbur's trapped foot. The two stood together a moment while the captain hooked the extra air tank to Wilbur's suit. Then, as Miss Pickerell stooped through the outside door of the lock, they hurried to the ship.

Miss Pickerell and the crew made it safely back to Earth. All of them became heroes. Mr. Haggerty, the member of the crew who had been left behind, had cured Miss Pickerell's cow and had decided to become a veterinarian. With her rocks from Mars, Miss Pickerell won the grand prize at the state fair.

Answer these questions.

1. Why did the captain, Wilbur, and Mr. Killian shake hands solemnly and respectfully?

2. Why did Miss Pickerell think that she was paralyzed? What was really wrong?

3. Why was the captain afraid to let Miss Pickerell leave the ship?

4. Why couldn't Wilbur return to the ship with the others?

5. What kept the others from going back for Wilbur?

6. How did Miss Pickerell save Wilbur?

Reading in Health

Use your paper to answer the questions below.

1. Look at the selection. What is the selection about?
2. Are there heads or subheads? What are they? What will each section be about?
3. Are any words in boldface or italic type? List them.
4. Skim the material and make a list of words that are unfamiliar to you. Write the meanings of these words by using clues in the sentence or a dictionary.
5. Read the selection. List the important details.
6. In your own words write a paragraph that summarizes the information in the selection. If possible, use the words that you listed as unfamiliar or use synonyms for these words.

Accidents Can Happen

Accidents can happen to anyone at any time. New shoes may form a blister, or an animal may bite without warning. If you know how to take care of small injuries, you will keep them from becoming large problems.

Blisters

Blisters are caused when something pinches or rubs the skin. If the blister is not broken, leave it alone. Opening a blister may cause an *infection,* or a sore. Keep the blister clean. It will go away by itself. If the blister is broken, wash it gently with soap and warm water. *Apply,* or place, a bandage on it and keep the blistered area clean.

Animal Bites

Most bites that people receive from animals come from healthy animals. However, if you are bitten by an animal, tell an adult. The animal will have to be checked for a serious disease called *rabies.* If the animal cannot be checked, a series of *inoculations,* or shots, will have to be taken.

To care for a bite, first wash the skin well with soap and water. Rinse the wound with clear running water. Cover with a clean bandage. Call the doctor *immediately,* or as soon as possible. The doctor will decide what else to do.

The Solar System

Isaac Asimov

Our solar system is very large. Sunlight must travel millions of miles to reach all of the planets in the solar system. However, the solar system is only a small part of the universe. This article tells some of the discoveries that have been made about the solar system.

The Planets and the Sun

On any clear day, you can see the sun in the sky. It is a shining ball of light. It is too bright to look at directly. It is 93 million miles (almost 150 million kilometers) away. However, it is still bright enough to light up the earth.

The earth goes around the sun. It makes one whole path around the sun in one year. A world that goes around the sun is called a **planet.** The earth is a planet. There are also eight other worlds moving around the sun. That means there are nine planets in all.

Each planet has a path in which it moves around the sun. The path is the planet's **orbit.** The sun, which was called "Sol" by the people of early Rome, is at the center of all the orbits of all the planets. For that reason, the sun and all the planets that go around it make up what is called the **solar system.**

The sun is far larger than all the planets put together. The planet that is closest to the sun is Mercury. Then come Venus and Earth. Our world is the third planet from the sun.

Beyond Earth, in order, are Mars, Jupiter, Saturn, Uranus, and Neptune. The last planet is Pluto. Pluto is the farthest from the sun.

Are there more planets beyond Pluto? Maybe, but no one has ever seen another. The farther a planet is from us, the harder it is for us to see it. Another planet beyond Pluto would be very far away. It would be so far away that finding it would be very hard indeed.

The Planets' Differences

The planets are different from each other in many ways. They are different in size. The earth is fairly large. Venus is smaller than the earth. Mars is quite a bit smaller.

Pluto is the smallest planet. Mercury, Venus, and Mars all seem to be made up of rock and metal. Earth is, too.

Four of the far planets, Jupiter, Saturn, Uranus, and Neptune, are giants. They are much larger than the earth. Jupiter is the largest. It is eleven times as wide as the earth. Jupiter has more matter in it than all

Page 180
Blue and white Viking Orbiter and the Lander it left on Mars

Page 181
Diagram of the planets of the solar system and some of their satellites

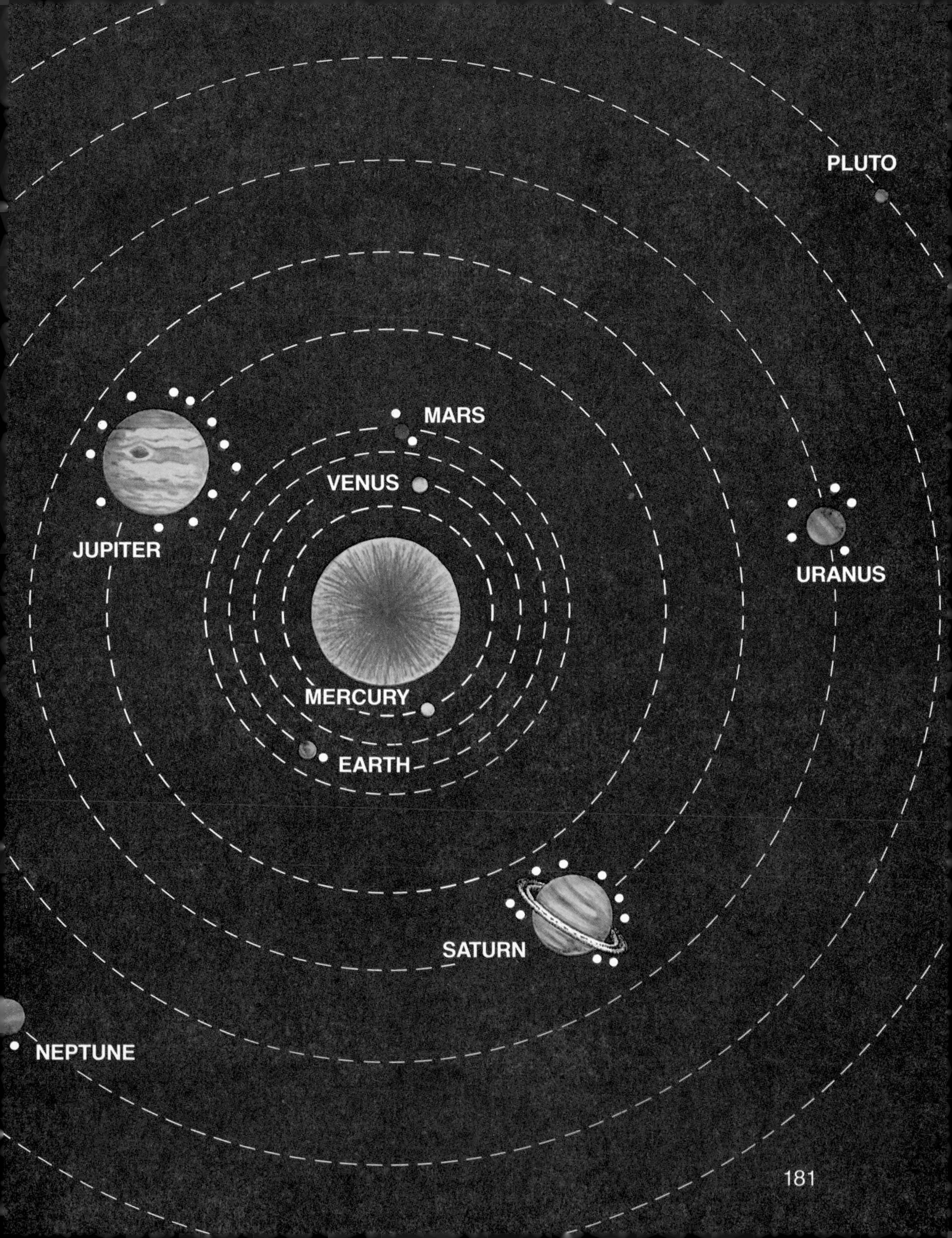

PLUTO

MARS

VENUS

JUPITER

URANUS

MERCURY

EARTH

SATURN

NEPTUNE

Earth and Sun rising over the surface of the moon; to the left of Earth is Venus; at the top and beginning from the left are Jupiter, Mercury, Mars, and Saturn

the other planets put together. Still, Jupiter is small compared to the sun.

The giant planets are not made of rock and metal. They are mostly made of light things, like gases.

The nearer a planet is to the sun, the hotter it is. Mercury is very, very hot. A piece of lead placed on this planet would melt. On the other hand, Pluto is very cold. It is so cold that air would freeze.

The sun's **gravity** pulls at all of the planets. Its pull on the close plan-

ets is very strong. Its pull is weaker with those planets that are farther out in space. The planets with the weaker pull from the sun move more slowly than the others.

The farther a planet is from the sun, the larger the orbit it has. The path of a planet far from the sun is like a large circle that is a little flat. This kind of path is called an **ellipse.** It takes a long, long time for the far planets to make one trip around the sun.

It takes the earth one year to

make one trip around the sun. Mars takes nearly two years. Jupiter takes twelve years. Saturn takes twenty-nine years. Uranus takes eighty-four years. Neptune takes 165 years. Pluto takes 248 years to go around the sun one time.

Mercury is very close to the sun. It moves around it in three months. Venus takes only seven months to go around the sun.

The Planets' Satellites

The planets move around the sun, which is much larger than they. Smaller bodies move around some of the planets. These smaller bodies are called **satellites.**

There are thirty-two known satellites in our solar system. They are part of the solar system, too. There are very likely other satellites, but they are so small that they have not yet been discovered.

Saturn and some of its satellites

Jupiter and some of its satellites

Earth has one satellite. It is the moon. It takes a month to make one trip around the earth. The word *month* comes from the word *moon*. The moon is closer to the earth than any other body. Venus is over a hundred times farther away from Earth than the moon is.

Because the moon is close to us, it looks very big. The planets seem like dots of light. However, the moon is really smaller than any of the planets. It is even smaller than Pluto, the smallest planet.

Still, the moon and the sun look just about the same size in the sky. The sun doesn't look larger than the moon because it is 400 times farther from the earth than the moon is. This makes it seem the same size to us.

As you can see, the solar system is a very large place. However, it is only a small part of the universe.

About the Author

Isaac Asimov is an American author of science-fiction and nonfiction books for children and adults. He has written nearly two hundred books. On some days he writes for eighteen hours. Sometimes he writes over fifty pages in one day. He makes science understandable to the average person.

Moon, Earth's satellite

Answer these questions.

1. What makes up the solar system?

2. Why would a planet that is beyond Pluto be hard to see?

3. Which planet is the smallest? Which is the hottest planet?

4. What are satellites? What is Earth's satellite called?

5. Why do the sun and the moon seem to be the same size when they are seen from the earth?

6. What makes up the universe?

Write on your own.

You are a space traveler. You are making a trip to the planet Pluto. The trip will take several years. Make a list of the things that you will take to keep busy during the trip. Remember that the things you take must not weigh very much.

How Do They Do It?

Edgar Fauver

People in shows do not just learn their lines and then go before the cameras. A lot of hard work from many different people comes first. This article is about some of the things that must be done before a show can be begun and some of the people who do these special jobs.

Muppet Construction Workshop   © 1978 Henson Associates, Inc.

TV shows and movies almost always tell stories. Most of these stories are about things that never happened. Yet these shows can often seem very real.

First the story is written like a play. Then actors learn their lines. They are told how and when to speak. They think about how to look and move.

Sometimes they almost do their jobs too well. Everything may seem too real. Have you ever closed your eyes in a movie? Have you ever cried? It may be hard to believe that the people are just playing parts. Don't worry. That blood you see isn't real.

Many other people help bring the stories to life. Some are in charge of lights. Others help with sound. Some people make furniture, sets, or clothes.

Some clothes are bought at stores that sell old things. However, stores don't have all the kinds of clothes that are needed. Does the story call for a hoop skirt? Is a space suit needed? Things like these must be made. Making them is a fine art. Everything must look just right.

Edith Head was well known for the costumes she made. For many years she was in charge of this kind of work at Paramount Studios in Hollywood, California.

Ms. Head's costumes helped show the story's setting. They also told things about the characters. A bandage said that someone was hurt. A badge said that a person was a police officer. Because Ms. Head's costumes were the very best, she won eight Oscars. An Oscar is the highest award given to people who work in movies.

Even characters can be made for movies. Some, like Jim Henson's Muppets, become real stars. Most of the Muppets are made of foam rubber. However, the oldest Muppet is made of green felt. His name is Kermit the Frog.

Henson's little friends are called

© 1978 Henson Associates, Inc.

Muppets for a reason. In some ways they are like puppets. In other ways they are like marionettes. Henson put these two words together to make the name Muppets.

A puppet fits over a hand like a glove. A marionette is worked with strings held from above. A Muppet's mouth works like a puppet's. The rest of it moves as freely as a marionette.

Most of the time, only one person works a puppet or a marionette. However, a Muppet often needs more than one person. The Muppet's head fits over one person's arm. The person's other arm wears the Muppet's glovelike arm and hand. Another person uses sticks to work the Muppet's other hand.

The two people hold the Muppet over their heads. Then they watch the Muppet on a TV. In that way they can see what they are doing.

After the Muppets made many TV shows, Henson used some of them in movies. These movies were seen by people all over the world.

One day Henson was asked to make a new Muppet. It was to be in a movie about space. That movie was *The Empire Strikes Back.* One of its stars was a Muppet called Yoda.

Frank Oz worked the Muppet Yoda for the movie. He sat in a little room under the stage. His arms reached up through holes in the floor. The stage was set to look like Yoda's swamp, so Oz's room grew very hot. Still, he made every move with great care. Yoda seemed very real.

Oz, who works other Muppets, likes to play tricks. One day a visitor popped up in Yoda's swamp. It was Miss Piggy. Everyone laughed at Oz's joke. Still, Miss Piggy's part had to be cut from the movie.

Some characters are made to look like real animals. They may be small, but they are filmed to look like giant animals.

Sometimes very large animals are built. Because they were seen with people, King Kong and the shark in the movie *Jaws* had to be huge for their parts.

Many props are smaller than they seem. Spaceships may look big, but they are really only small models. They are made to look real in every way. If one were filmed next to an orange, everyone could see that it is small. However, filmed against a background of stars, it looks huge.

These movie tricks are called special effects. Some of the harder tricks are done by computer. A computer may work both a spaceship model and the camera. The camera follows the model's every move. They both may glide over another model, a planet. This part of the film is planned very cleverly. Everything looks as if it were real.

Watch closely the next time you go to a movie. Everything may look real, but not everything will be. Look closely at the set and the props. Check out the characters and the clothes they wear. See if you can tell what is real and what is really a movie trick.

© Lucasfilm Ltd. (LFL) 1980. All rights reserved.

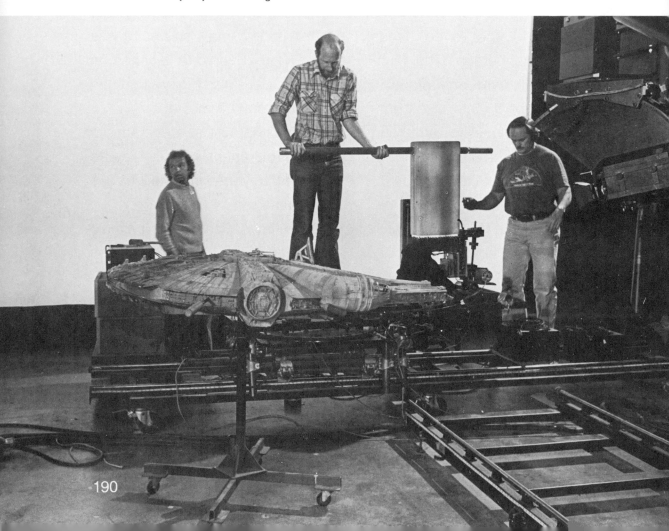

Answer these questions.

1. What are two examples of ways in which costumes tell things about characters?

2. What awards did Edith Head win as a costume designer?

3. Why does Jim Henson call his characters Muppets?

4. How do the people who work the Muppets know that everything is going well?

5. Why was the film of Miss Piggy not used in "The Empire Strikes Back"?

6. What things are filmed to look like spaceships in the movies? What machines are used to make these spaceships look real?

Reading Clothing Labels

Read the following vocabulary words. Be sure you understand their meanings before you begin this lesson.

bleach   to make white with chemicals
cycle   a period of time
mild   gentle or soft
promptly   quickly
tumble   to roll around

Before washing clothes, it is very important to check all of the clothes for the washing directions label. Many times this tag is on the inside of the neck, waist, or sleeve of clothing. The following labels are examples of the kinds of cleaning instructions that might be found on these labels. Some of the labels explain what kind of cloth or material was used in making the clothes. By reading the directions on the label and following them correctly, clothes will not be torn, shrunk, or faded.

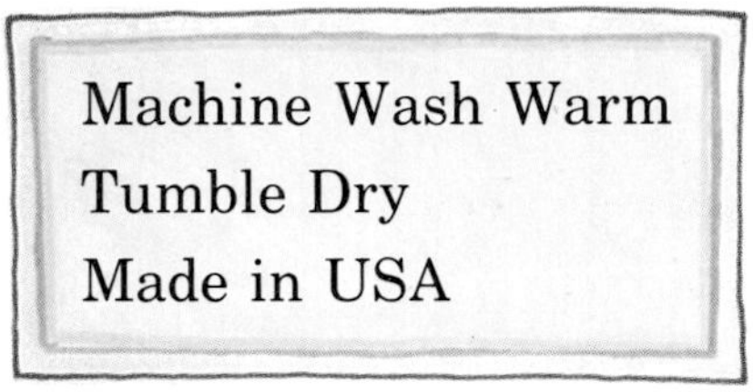

Machine Wash Warm
Tumble Dry
Made in USA

100% Silk
Dry-Clean Only

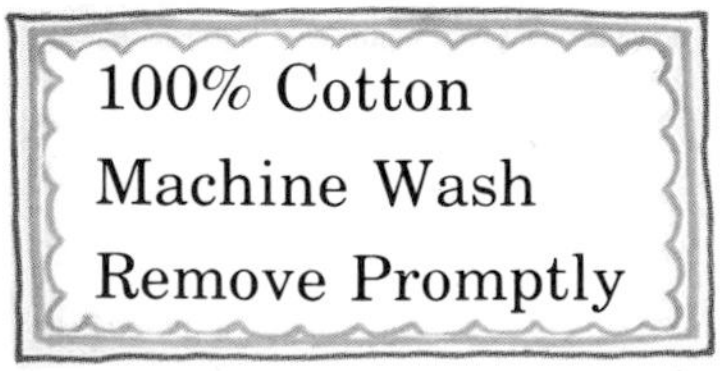

100% Cotton
Machine Wash
Remove Promptly

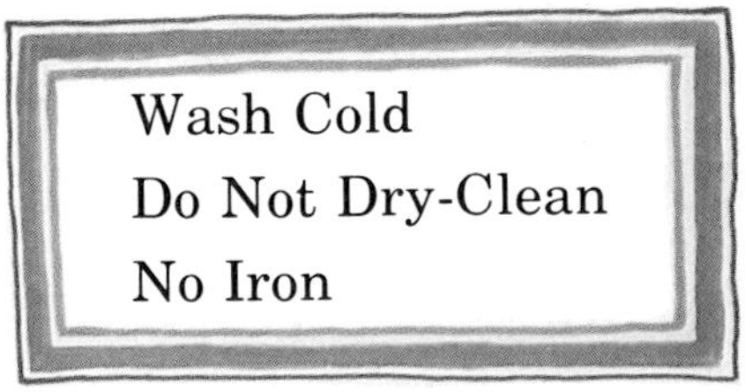

Wash Cold
Do Not Dry-Clean
No Iron

Hand Wash	50% Nylon
Mild Soap	50% Cotton
No Bleach	Gentle Cycle
Dry Flat	Hang Dry

On your paper answer these questions.

1. Look at the fifth label. Do you think that this label would be found on a very strong kind of cloth? Why?

2. If a label reads "remove promptly," what does it mean that the owner should do?
   a. leave the clothes in the dryer a long time
   b. take the clothes out of the dryer quickly
   c. leave the clothes in the washer a long time
   d. take the clothes out of the house quickly

3. The words "wash cold" appear on label 4. What does this mean?
   a. only wash when you are cold
   b. only wash when the clothes are cold
   c. only wash when it is cold outside
   d. only wash these clothes with cold water

194

Thank You, Jackie Robinson

Barbara Cohen

At one time the Dodgers baseball team was based in Brooklyn, New York. In the 1940s and 1950s Jackie Robinson was one of the greatest players on the Brooklyn Dodgers team. In this story a young boy meets the famous Jackie Robinson when he tries to get a special present for a very special friend.

Today, Friday, I asked my mother for my allowance and for my three dollars and fifty cents that she was saving for me.

"I think that's too much to spend on a present for Davy," Mother said. "A dollar would be plenty."

"Mother!" I exclaimed. I was surprised. "If I had a thousand dollars, it wouldn't be too much to spend."

"It's your money. I think you're crazy. You don't need to spend money to show love."

"It's the only way," I said. "They won't let me in to see him."

"It's your money," she repeated. She shook her head, but then she gave it to me.

The next day, Saturday, was of course the busiest day of the week at the inn. Even during July and August, the slow months, Saturday was sometimes busy. I was lucky. On this Saturday there was a wedding reception. What with Davy sick and the new cook not quite up to preparing a whole banquet, my mother had to be in six places at once. She really didn't have time to worry about us. It was one of those days when she just wanted us to go away somewhere and not bother her until it was time for Sara and me to help dish out the meal. I told her I'd come home before dark.

My mother nodded absently. "Have fun," she said and hurried off.

I had gone into the kitchen real early in the morning, before anyone else was up. I had made myself a couple of egg-salad sandwiches. I had them and my money and the new baseball in its little cardboard box. I walked the mile and a half to the bus station. There'd be no place to leave my bike if I rode there. I took the bus into New York City. I took a subway to Ebbets Field.

You could see flags flying above the ball park when you climbed up out of the subway station. You had to walk three blocks and there you were. Inside, it was as it always had been, as bright and green as ever, far away from the dirty streets that surrounded it, far away from all the world. In the excitement of being there, I almost forgot about Davy for a moment. I almost forgot why I had come. When the Cubs' pitcher, Warren Hacker, began to warm up, I turned to Davy to ask him if he thought Shotton was going to give Jackie's sore heel a rest that day, but Davy wasn't there. I remembered.

I thought maybe I'd better start trying right away. My chances might be better during batting practice than they would be later. I took my ball out of its box. I hid the box under my seat. Then I walked around to the first-base side and climbed all the way down to the box seats right behind the dugout. I leaned over the rail. Billy Cox was trotting back to the dugout from home plate. Erskine had been throwing to him.

I swallowed my heart, which seemed to be beating in my throat. I called out, "Billy, hey Billy," waving my ball as hard and as high as I could. I was scared, though. My voice wasn't very loud. I don't think Billy Cox heard me. He went into the dugout.

This was getting me nowhere. I had to try something else before the game began and I'd really lost my chance. I looked around to see if there were any ushers nearby. None were in sight. It was kind of early. The place hadn't really started to fill up yet.

I climbed up on the railing and then hauled myself onto the roof of the dugout.

I could have stood up and walked across the dugout roof to the edge. I figured if I did that, an usher surely would see me. I crawled across the roof on my stomach until I came to the edge. Then I leaned over.

It was really very nice in the dugout. I had always kind

of pictured it as being dug out of the dirt. I was surprised
when I saw it had real walls and a floor and benches and a
water cooler. Only trouble was, there were just a couple of
guys in there—Eddie Miksis, and Billy Cox, whom I'd seen
out on the field a few minutes before. I was disappointed. I
had certainly hoped for Campy's signature, and Gil Hodges's, and Pee Wee Reese's, and of course Jackie Robinson's.
I figured Davy would be pleased with Miksis and Billy Cox,
since their names on a ball would be more than he'd ever
expected.

No matter how hard I swallowed, my heart was still
stuck in my throat. "Eddie," I called. "Eddie, Billy." Hardly
any sound came out of my mouth at all.

Then all of a sudden I heard a voice calling real loud.
Whoever it was didn't have any trouble getting the sound

out of *his* mouth. "Hey you, kid, get down off that roof," the voice said. "What do you think you're doing?" I sat up and turned around. An angry usher was standing at the foot of the aisle, right by the railing, screaming at me. "Get yourself off that roof," he shouted. "Right now, or I'll throw you out of the ball park."

I crawled down as fast as I could. Boy, was I a mess. My pants and my striped shirt were covered with dust and dirt from that roof. I guess my face and arms weren't any too clean, either. I looked like a bum.

"I'm going to throw you out anyway," the usher said, "because you don't have a ticket."

I got real mad when I heard him say that. I had suddenly found my voice. I was scared of the ball players, but this usher didn't frighten me one bit. I pulled my ticket stub out of my pocket. "See?" I said. "I certainly do have a ticket."

He made as if to take it out of my hand. I guess he wanted to look at it close, to make sure it was a stub from that day and not an old one I carried around in my pocket for emergencies. However, I pulled my hand back.

"Oh, no, you don't," I said. "You can't take this ticket away from me. You won't give it back to me. Then you'll throw me out because I don't have a ticket!"

"You crazy, kid?" he asked, shaking his head. "This is what I get for working in Ebbets Field. A bunch of crazy people. Next year I'm applying for a job at the Polo Grounds."

I turned away from him and leaned over the rail.

"I better not see you on that roof again," the usher said. "I'll have my eye out for you. So will all the other ushers."

"Don't worry," I said.

Then I felt his hand on my shoulder. "As a matter of fact, kid," he said, "I think I'll take you to your seat where you belong. Up in the stands where you can't make any trouble!"

Well, right then and there the whole deal would have gone up in smoke if old Jackie Robinson himself had not come trotting out onto the field from the dugout that very second. "Hey, Jackie," I called, "hey, Jackie," in a voice as loud as a crack of thunder.

He glanced over in the direction he could tell my voice was coming from. I began to wave, still calling, "Jackie, hey, Jackie."

He lifted up his hand, gave one wide wave, and smiled. "Hey, kid," he called. He continued on his way to the batting cage. In another instant he'd have been too busy with batting practice to pay any attention to me.

"Sign my ball," I screamed. "Sign my ball."

He seemed to stop briefly. I took this as a good sign. "You have to," I went on. "Please, please, you have to."

"He doesn't have to do anything," the usher said. "That's Jackie Robinson. Everyone knows that he doesn't have to do anything."

I went right on screaming.

"Come on, kid," the usher said, "we're getting out of here." He was a big usher who must have weighed about eight hundred pounds. He began pulling me. He couldn't shut me up, though.

"Please, Jackie, please," I went right on screaming.

It worked. Or something worked. If not my screaming, then maybe the sight of that monster usher trying to pull me up the aisle and little old me pulling against him for dear life.

"Let the kid go," Jackie Robinson said when he got to the railing. "All he wants is an autograph."

"He's a fresh kid," the usher said. He let me go.

I waved my ball in Jackie Robinson's face. "Gee, thanks, Mr. Robinson," I said. "Sign it, please."

"You got a pen?" he asked.

"A pen?" I could have kicked myself. "A pen?" I'd forgotten a pen! I turned to the usher. "You got a pen?"

"As it happens, I don't have one," the usher replied.

"Wait here," I said. "Wait right here, Mr. Robinson. I'll go find one."

Jackie Robinson laughed. "Sorry, kid, but I've got work to do. Another time, maybe."

"Please, Mr. Robinson," I said. "It's for my friend. My friend, Davy."

"Well, let Davy come and get his own autographs," he said. "Why should you do his dirty work for him?"

"He can't come," I said. The words came rushing out of me, one on top of the other. I had to tell Jackie Robinson all about it, before he went away. "Davy can't come because he's sick. He had a heart attack."

"A heart attack?" Jackie Robinson asked. "A kid had a heart attack?"

"He's not a kid," I explained. "He's sixty years old. He's my best friend. He's always loved the Dodgers. Lately he's loved them more than ever."

"How did this Davy get to be your best friend?" he asked.

So I told him. I told him everything, or as near to everything as I could tell in five minutes. I told him how Davy worked for my mother, and how I had no father. It was Davy who took me to my first ball game. I told him how they wouldn't let me into the hospital to see Davy, and how we had always talked about catching a ball that was hit into the stands and getting it autographed.

Jackie listened silently, nodding every once in a while. When I was done at last, he said, "Well, now, kid, I'll tell you what. You keep this ball you brought with you. Keep it to play with. Also, borrow a pen from someone. Come back to the dugout the minute, the very second, the game is over. I'll get you a real ball, one we played with. I'll get all the guys to autograph it for you."

"Make sure it's one you hit," I said.

What nerve. I should have fainted dead away just be-

cause Jackie Robinson had spoken to me. However, he
didn't seem to care.

"OK," he said, "*if* I hit one."

"You will," I said, "you will."

He did! He broke the ball game wide open in the sixth
inning when he hit a double to left field, scoring Rackley
and Duke Snider. He scored himself when the Cubs pitcher,
Warren Hacker, tried to pick him off second base. However,
Hacker overthrew, and Jackie, with that incredible speed he
had, ran all the way home. The Dodgers scored six runs.

They scored them all in the sixth inning. They beat the Cubs, 6-1. They were hot, really hot, that day and that year.

I didn't really watch the game as closely as I had all the others I'd been to see. I couldn't. My mind was on too many other things—on Jackie Robinson, on what was going to happen after the game was over, on that monster usher who I feared would yet find some way of spoiling things for me, but above all on Davy and the fact that he was missing all of the excitement.

Plus I had to worry about getting hold of a pen. You could buy little pencils at the ball park for keeping box scores, but no pens.

It didn't look to me like the guys in the stands where I was sitting had pens with them anyway. I decided to walk over to the seats along the first-base line to see if any of those fans looked more like pen owners.

On my way I ran into this guy selling soda. I decided to buy one in order to wash down the two egg-salad sandwiches I had eaten during the third inning.

This guy had a pen in his pocket. As a matter of fact, he had two of them. "Look," I said to him as I paid him for my soda, "could I borrow one of those pens?"

"Sure," he said, handing it to me after he had put my money into his change machine. He stood there, waiting, like he expected me to hand it back to him after I was done with it.

"Look," I said again, "maybe I could sort of buy it from you."

"Buy it from me? You mean the pen?"

"Yeah."

"What do you want my pen for?"

"I need it because Jackie Robinson promised me that after the game he and all the other guys would autograph a ball for me."

"You don't say," the man remarked. I could tell he didn't believe me.

"It's true," I said. "Anyway, are you going to sell me your pen?"

"Sure. For a dollar."

I didn't have a dollar. I'd have to try something else. I started to walk away.

"Oh, don't be silly, kid," he called to me. "Here, take the pen. Keep it." It was a nice pen. It was shaped like a bat. On it, it said, "Ebbets Field, Home of the Brooklyn Dodgers."

"Hey, mister, thanks," I said. "That's real nice of you." It seemed to me I ought to do something for him. I added, "I think I'd like another soda." He sold me another. Between sipping first from one and then from the other and trying to watch the game, I made very slow progress down to the dugout. I got there just before the game ended in the top of the ninth.

I stood at the railing near the dugout, waiting. Sure enough, Jackie Robinson appeared around the corner of the building only a minute or two after Preacher Roe pitched that final out. All around me people were getting up to leave the ball park. A lot of them stopped when they saw Jackie Robinson come to the rail to talk to me. Roy Campanella, Pee Wee Reese, and Gil Hodges were with him.

"Hi, kid," Jackie Robinson said. He was carrying a ball. It was covered with signatures. "Pee Wee here had a pen."

"A good thing, too," Pee Wee said, "because most of the other guys left the field already."

"These guys wanted to meet Davy's friend," Jackie Robinson said.

By that time, Preacher Roe had joined us at the railing. Jackie handed him the ball. "Hey, Preacher," he said, "got enough strength left in that arm to sign this ball for Davy's friend here?"

"Got a pen?" Preacher Roe asked.

I handed him the pen the man had given me. I was glad I hadn't gone through all the trouble of getting it for nothing.

"Not much room left on this ball," Roe said. He squirmed his name into a little empty space beneath Duke Snider's. Then he handed me both the pen and the ball. Everybody was waving programs and pens in the faces of the ball players who stood by the railing. Before they signed any of them, they all shook my hand. Jackie Robinson did, too. I stood there, holding Davy's ball and watching while those guys signed the programs of the other fans. Finally, though, they'd had enough. They smiled and waved their hands and walked away. Jackie Robinson was the last one into the dugout. Before he went around the corner, he turned and waved to me.

I waved back. "Thank you, Jackie Robinson," I called. "Thanks for everything." He nodded and smiled. I guess he heard me. I'm glad I remembered my manners before it was too late.

Soon everyone was gone. I looked down at the ball in my hands. Right between the rows of red seaming, Jackie Robinson had written, above his own signature, "For Davy. Get well soon." Then all the others had put their names around that.

I took the ball I had brought out of the box and put it in my pocket. I put the ball Jackie Robinson had given me in the box. Then I went home.

Answer these questions.

1. Who told this story? Where did most of the story take place?

2. What did the boy plan to do at the baseball stadium?

3. Who is Davy?

4. What happened when the boy first tried to get the ball autographed?

5. Did the boy know that he was not allowed to crawl out on the dugout roof? How do you know?

6. Who was Jackie Robinson? How did he help the boy?

Something Strange on Vacation

Elizabeth Levy

Jill and Gwen are friends who are spending summer vacation near the beach. They want to win one of the weekly contests for building the best sandcastle. Something strange begins to happen, though. Gwen and Jill must find out who has been wrecking their castles in order to keep them from winning.

"This week we're going to win," said Gwen. She
and Jill ran down to the beach. Every Sunday there was
a sandcastle contest. Gwen and Jill had built a lot of
castles. However, they had never won.

"I'll help you," said Gwen's little sister, Nan.

"No," said Gwen. "You will only make a mess."

Fletcher started to dig a hole in the sand to keep
cool. He was Gwen's dog.

"Why don't you help Fletcher dig a hole?" said
Gwen.

"I don't want to," said Nan. She walked off down
the beach.

Gwen and Jill worked on their sandcastle all

morning. For once their drip towers soared instead of drooped.

"I'm hungry," said Jill. "Let's go eat."

"What about Fletcher?" asked Gwen. Fletcher was asleep in his hole.

"Let him sleep," said Jill. "He's tired."

"He's always tired," said Gwen.

When Gwen and Jill came back after lunch, Fletcher was lying smack on top of their castle. He had squashed it. Only one tower remained.

"Oh, no!" cried Gwen. "You bad dog!"

Jill dragged Fletcher off the squashed castle.

Gwen stared at the ruins. She bent down and picked up a crust of bread that had been under Fletcher. A tiny piece of salami was on the crust.

"Salami," said Gwen, tapping her braces. She always tapped her braces whenever something strange was going on.

"You can't be hungry," said Jill. "We just had lunch."

"No, I mean that Fletcher loves salami," Gwen explained. "It's the only thing that could make him move. Someone put some on our castle so he'd wreck it."

"Do you think someone who really wanted to win might have cheated?" asked Jill.

Gwen nodded her head. "Come on. I bet it was someone nearby."

George was the closest. His castle was square and neat.

"What did you have for lunch today?" asked Gwen.

"Peanut butter," said George. "Why?"

"Never mind," said Gwen.

Gwen and Jill walked down the beach. They questioned everyone.

Philip said he had a ham sandwich for lunch.

"I didn't have time for lunch," said Joanne. "I was too busy finishing my moat."

Nobody on the beach had eaten a salami sandwich. At least nobody told Gwen and Jill about eating a salami sandwich.

Gwen and Jill watched as the judges gave first prize to Joanne.

"Too bad your dog squashed your castle," said Joanne as she walked by. She looked very happy.

"Maybe it was just an accident," said Jill sadly.

"Or maybe that's what Joanne wants us to think," said Gwen.

The next Sunday was the last contest before the big July Fourth final. Gwen and Jill worked slowly and carefully until their castle was nearly perfect. It had tunnels that crisscrossed and eight drip towers. They took Fletcher with them when they went up to the house for lunch.

When they came back to the beach, they couldn't believe their eyes.

Their castle was wrecked! Again! All the towers had been pushed down. The tunnels had been crushed in. Jill sat down next to the ruins. She started to cry. Fletcher tried to lick her tears away.

"This time nobody can say it was an accident," Gwen said angrily. She checked the ruins. Strange webbed tracks led away from their castle to the ocean.

"That's who wrecked our castle," said Gwen. She pointed to the tracks.

"A sea monster?" whispered Jill.

"No," said Gwen. "Those are flipper tracks. The person who wrecked our castle was wearing rubber flippers."

Gwen tapped her braces. "These tracks aren't very big," she said. "They aren't very deep, either. In school we learned that you can tell how heavy an animal is by how deep its tracks are."

Gwen circled the ruins. She tapped her braces. Fletcher followed her.

"I've got it!" cried Gwen. "It was a skinny . . . salami-eating . . . flipper-footed fink!"

"Philip's skinny," said Jill. "So's Joanne. So is George. Lots of kids on this beach are skinny."

Gwen stopped. She looked at the track. She pointed to a trademark shape in the middle.

"It looks like a shark," said Gwen. "There is a piece missing from one of the toes. If we find the flippers that match these tracks, we can tell the judges."

Nearby, George was making a round castle. It had seaweed flags.

Gwen and Jill ran over. "Did you use flippers to get that seaweed?" asked Gwen.

"No," said George, "I don't own any."

"George could be lying," said Gwen as they walked away. "He says he doesn't own flippers. He could be hiding them."

"I don't think George is lying," said Jill. They stopped at Joanne's castle.

"Are those your flippers?" asked Gwen. She tapped her braces.

"Yes," said Joanne. "Why are you tapping your braces?"

Casually Jill turned over Joanne's flippers. They had a starfish mark on them. Jill shook her head. "No shark. Come on, Gwen," she said. Joanne looked puzzled. Gwen and Jill walked away.

Next they found Philip. He was building an octagon castle.

"Where are your flippers, Philip?" asked Gwen.

"Have you flipped?" said Philip. "I don't have any flippers."

Gwen and Jill checked every flipper they could find. None matched.

George's round castle with the seaweed flags won that week's contest.

"We never win," said Jill sadly. "We never even have a chance."

Gwen shook her fist. "We're going to build the best castle for the July Fourth contest. We're going to make *sure* it doesn't get wrecked."

All week Gwen and Jill studied drawings of castles. They gathered shells to put on the castle. They found beach glass to use as windows.

"Have you come up with a plan to catch the person who keeps wrecking our castles?" asked Jill.

"No," said Gwen. "I still don't even know who it is."

"You'd better think fast," said Jill. "We don't have much time."

On July Fourth Gwen and Jill got up at dawn. So did George, Philip, Joanne, and many other people who wanted to enter.

The prizes for the July Fourth contest were a trophy in the shape of a sandcastle and a dragon kite to fly on the beach.

As they worked, the sun got very hot. Gwen and Jill were halfway finished when Fletcher started to dig a hole to keep cool.

"I'm hot, too," said Jill. "I need a swim. Let's take turns. That way one of us can guard our castle."

"Suppose we both hid in the water," said Gwen. "With our masks and our snorkels we can stay close by and watch. The castle wrecker will think our castle has been left all alone."

"They could wreck it before we got out," said Jill.

"We can be out in time," said Gwen. "We'll be able to see them. However, they won't see us."

Gwen and Jill put on their flippers, masks, and snorkels. They floated just a little way off shore.

After a while they saw someone wearing flippers and a mask. The person came up to their castle. Fletcher stood up. He wagged his tail.

Gwen and Jill raced out of the water. The castle wrecker took off down the beach. The person ran strangely because of the flippers.

Gwen and Jill took off their flippers. They flew down the beach after the person. Fletcher followed.

Fletcher took a flying leap. He grabbed a flipper. The castle wrecker fell in the sand.

Gwen and Jill ran to see who it was. It was Nan!

Fletcher was licking her fingers.

"You're the salami-eating fink!" shouted Gwen. "My own sister."

Nan blushed a deep red. "It was just an accident. At least the first time it was an accident," she said. "I was mad because you wouldn't let me help. I dumped my sandwich on your castle to make it look like a mess."

"I bet you ate salami again today," said Gwen. She tapped her braces.

"How did you know that?" asked Nan.

"Because Fletcher chased you," said Gwen. "He thought you were going to give him more salami. Why did you keep wrecking our castles?"

"You never let me help you do anything," said Nan.

"It was a really mean thing to do," said Jill. "We don't have time to talk. We have to finish our castle."

Gwen and Jill worked quickly to finish their castle. As a final touch they made a figure of Fletcher guarding the castle gates.

Gwen and Jill won first prize. George, Philip, and Joanne congratulated them. Gwen and Jill let them take turns flying their beautiful kite.

As punishment for knocking down the castles, Gwen's mother wouldn't let Nan see the fireworks. Everyone else sat on the beach and watched.

Fletcher was scared of fireworks. He hid under Nan's bed. Nan and Fletcher shared salami all through the fireworks. The more Fletcher ate, the less scared he was.

Answer these questions.

1. Why did the girls question the people on the beach as to what they ate for lunch and whether they had used flippers?

2. Why did the girls take Fletcher with them when they went to lunch after building the second sandcastle?

3. What was Gwen's plan to find out who was wrecking their sandcastles?

4. Who was the castle wrecker? Why did the person wreck the castles?

5. What prizes did Jill and Gwen receive? What happened to the castle-wrecker?

Barefoot Days

In the morning, very early,
    That's the time I love to go
Barefoot where the fern grows curly
    And grass is cool between each toe,
      On a summer morning-O!
      On a summer morning!

That is when the birds go by
    Up the sunny slopes of air,
And each rose has a butterfly
    Or a golden bee to wear;
And I am glad in every toe—
      Such a summer morning-O!
      Such a summer morning!

Rachel Field

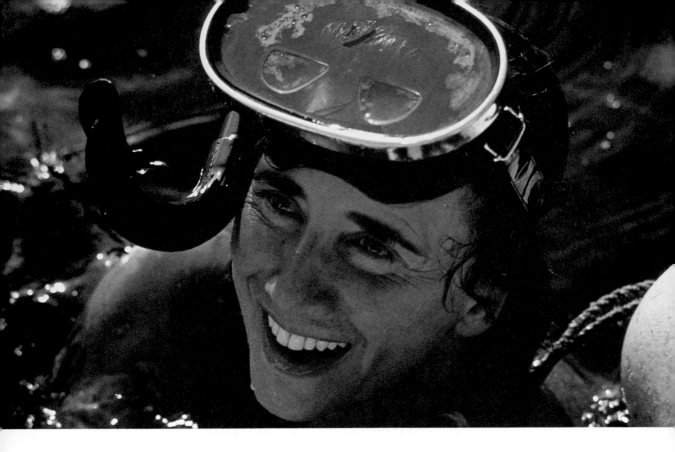

True Adventures of Eugenie Clark: Shark Lady

Ann McGovern

As a young girl, Eugenie Clark often visited the aquarium
in New York City and promised herself that one day she
would swim with the sharks. In college she went around the
world studying the oceans' fish. At her sea laboratory in Florida she found that sharks can learn which board to push with
their noses in order to get food. The most difficult question
that Eugenie has studied may seem a very simple one: Do
sharks ever sleep?

Into the Caves of the "Sleeping" Sharks

Eugenie Clark's dream of becoming a teacher came true. She became a teacher at a college. She shared her great knowledge and her love of fish with her classes. Her students brought their friends to hear Eugenie Clark talk about her adventures in faraway places.

"Study what fascinates you the most," she told them.

As for herself, she never stopped studying and learning. There was always an important task to work on, something new to discover, or some mystery to solve.

For one thing, there was the puzzle of the "sleeping" sharks.

Eugenie heard about them from an old friend, Ramon Bravo, an underwater naturalist and photographer from Mexico. He sent word that big sharks had been discovered in a cave below the sea. These sharks seemed to be sleeping!

He told her that the sharks were not nurse sharks. The nurse sharks are slow moving and are often found in caves. However, these were requiem sharks. This kind of shark is a fast swimmer.

Would she come and see for herself?

If it were really true, it certainly would be surprising, Eugenie thought. Everyone thought these sharks had to keep moving to keep water flowing over their gills. Water has oxygen, which all sharks need to stay alive.

Eugenie could take only a few days away from her teaching to go to Mexico.

When she got there she dived to the cave. She saw many beautiful fish in the cave, but no sharks. Then just as she was coming out, a shark slipped into the cave.

"I don't know how I can prove to you that these sharks do

sleep in these caves," Ramon said. "Maybe I have to put them in pajamas and give them an alarm clock." He begged her to return as soon as she could.

The next year she was back with a team made up of several of her pupils, Mexican divers, photographers, and her nineteen-year-old daughter, Aya.

This time she saw the sharks in the caves.

"It was really unbelievable," Eugenie wrote in a magazine. "There I was, face to face with one of the sea's most deadly denizens, in the most dangerous situation possible—the shark, crowded, backed into a corner—and I'd never been more thrilled. It was an unforgettable moment in my life."

There was so much Eugenie wanted to learn. The Mexican divers told her that these sharks could be touched, even lifted gently, without becoming dangerous.

Sometimes when they were poked, the sharks would swim away. Sometimes, they settled back to their sleeplike state again.

Why? Why do big sharks stop swimming and go into this state? From her studies, Eugenie knew that it took more energy for one of these sharks to *stop* swimming than to keep on swimming. When a shark is at rest, it has to work harder to keep the water flowing through its gills.

Eugenie and her team searched for answers in the caves. They noticed that the sharks in the caves were very clean. Their skin was free of parasites, tiny animals that grow on the skin of big fish. One day Eugenie saw a little remora fish cleaning a shark in a cave. The little fish was going in and out of each gill opening, removing parasites. Then it nibbled away parasites all over the shark's head and down the shark's big body!

Could these caves be cleaning stations for sharks? It certainly looked like it.

There was so much to learn and so little time left. In a few days she had to return to her classes.

Anita George, one of Eugenie's pupils, wanted to get some last-minute notes on the "sleeping" sharks in the cave.

Two divers went down with her to the cave. Anita took notes on her special clipboard.

One of the divers flashed a bright light to take a picture with an underwater camera. Perhaps it was the light that did it. The shark woke up! It swept toward the opening of the cave, ramming its tail into Anita. It almost knocked off her face mask.

The shark was coming right toward her! She had only one thing with which to defend herself—her clipboard. She used it to push the big shark aside!

That night nobody got much sleep.

Time was up. There were no more days left for new adventures, or to find answers to questions.

The puzzle of the "sleeping" sharks was still a puzzle.

The Puzzle of the "Sleeping" Sharks

The next summer Eugenie and her team came back to the "sleeping" shark caves of Mexico.

Would they find the answers to the puzzle this time? Their tests had shown that the water in the caves *was* at times different from the water in the open sea. There was more oxygen, for one thing. Also, fresh water was flowing slowly up into the caves from streams under the ocean floor.

"Perhaps there is something in the water to make the sharks groggy," Eugenie thought.

"Perhaps our 'sleeping' sharks are drawn into the caves first to get cleaned, and second to enjoy the pleasant sensations," Dr. Clark wrote.

Did the sharks really sleep in the caves? The more Eugenie studied them, the more she thought they didn't. When Eugenie and Anita were in the caves, the sharks' eyes followed their every move.

Eugenie wanted to find out more about the sleeplike state. "Do fish sleep the way we sleep," she wondered, "the way other animals sleep?"

"It's very difficult to make tests on fish," Eugenie said. "We're still working on ways it can be done with sharks in captivity and with sharks in the open sea."

Eugenie wrote in the magazine article: "Perhaps in deeper waters, in other parts of the world, requiem sharks also sleep."

She was right. In 1976, Eugenie was invited to Japan. Anita George came, too, and this time Eugenie took along her stepfather, Nobusan. He was over seventy years old and was a wonderful help. He spoke Japanese and he also learned to keep charts of the breathing rates of sharks.

Eugenie and her team dived in many places. In one bay Eugenie and Anita saw over one hundred sharks—more than they had ever seen before at one time! Some were swimming around in the shallow end of the bay. Eugenie and Anita stood in the water taking notes while sharks swam around them.

Some of the sharks were in caves, piled on top of each other. They seemed to be asleep!

Eugenie found two different kinds of "sleeping" sharks in Japan. One of them was a white-tip requiem shark. The other was a white-tip reef shark. It spends a good deal of time on the bottom of the reef. Perhaps there were other reasons why this shark got into a sleeplike state. More tests had to be made. More sharks had to be studied.

Once a scientist took Eugenie to see thirty sharks in another cave not far from Tokyo. Eugenie swam around, petting them, and they didn't wake up.

At the end of the summer, Eugenie returned to her classes, the puzzle still not solved.

"Where will you go next to find the answer to the puzzle of the 'sleeping' sharks?" her class asked her.

"I hear that in the Red Sea there is a cave." Eugenie smiled. "And in that cave there are five 'sleeping' sharks. They are white-tip reef sharks, the same kind of sharks I saw in Japan. This summer I'll go back to the Red Sea.

"It's like a puzzle," Eugenie explained to her class. "You think you have the pieces put together and then, suddenly, one piece doesn't fit, and you're off on something else."

About the Author

Ann McGovern has written books for young people on many different subjects. Her hobbies are traveling and scuba diving. Many of her stories are about the places she has visited. She lives in New York with her family.

Answer these questions.

1. What mystery is Eugenie Clark trying to solve?

2. Why was it amazing for big sharks to be in a sleeplike state?

3. What did Eugenie and her team notice about the remora fish and the sharks? What might this mean?

4. What was different about the water in the caves where the sharks were "sleeping"?

5. Why didn't Eugenie think the sharks were sleeping?

6. Will "sleeping" sharks be found in places other than Mexico, Japan, and the Red Sea? Why do you think so?

Write on your own.

Pretend that you are a reporter. You are meeting some divers as they leave a ship. The divers have just found a treasure. Write sentences that answer the following questions. What happened? To whom did it happen? When did it happen? Where did it happen? How did it happen? Why did they go searching? Use the answers to write the first paragraph of a news story about the discovery.

Reading in Science

Use your paper to complete the exercise below.

1. Look at the selection. What is the selection about?
2. Are there heads or subheads? What are they? What will each section be about?
3. Are any words in boldface or italic type? List them.
4. Skim the material and make a list of words that are unfamiliar to you. Write the meanings of these words by using clues in the sentence or a dictionary.
5. Read the selection. List the important details.
6. In your own words write a paragraph that summarizes the information in the selection. If possible, use the words that you listed as unfamiliar or use synonyms for these words.

Sponges

Sponges are often used to wipe up spills. A sponge, however, is a very simple kind of animal.

What Makes Up a Sponge?

Each sponge is made of two parts. One part is the skeleton. A sponge's skeleton is not like the skeletons of other animals. It is made of a nonliving material. The skeleton is what we use to clean things.

The other part of the sponge is the cells. The cells are like tiny rooms. They store food for the sponge. Sponges do not have a certain amount of cells. That is why sponges have no certain size or shape. In general, sponges look like blobs.

The holes in a sponge are important to the life of the sponge and to other animals. Sponges live in water, which flows through these holes *continuously,* or without stopping. The water brings food to the holes, which trap the food. The holes may also be homes for small plants and animals, such as shrimp and crabs.

How Are Sponges Used?

When a sponge is out of water, the cells die and the skeleton remains. The skeleton can then be used. Today, rubber and other materials are used to make *artificial* sponges. These sponges have holes that soak up water and soap.

Vocabulary Review

On your paper write **a, b, c,** or **d** to show the item that best completes the sentence.

1. A filthy dress is one that is soiled, or _____.
   a. darling   c. dirty
   b. torn   d. new

2. The kite string was a mess; it was tangled and _____.
   a. twisted   c. twinkly
   b. dirty   d. amazing

3. Actors' costumes are their stage _____.
   a. clues   c. features
   b. smiles   d. clothes

4. Many gases make up the earth's atmosphere, or _____.
   a. oceans   c. tables
   b. friends   d. air

5. The ruins of a building are the _____.
   a. occupants   c. remains
   b. rewards   d. boards

6. A green fern is a kind of _____.
   a. plant   c. plaza
   b. road   d. toy

7. One's signature is made by signing one's _____.
   a. name   c. uncle
   b. address   d. neighbor

Books to Read

Cleary, Beverly   *Henry and Ribsy*

Henry and his dog Ribsy seem to have more adventures than should be their share. However, things always seem to turn out right for them.

Nash, Ogden   *Custard and Company*

Custard is a cowardly dragon who lives in Belinda's room. When faced with danger, Custard surprises himself and Belinda. Custard's story is only one in this collection of humorous poems.

Lasky, Kathryn   *My Island Grandma*

Abbey often visits her grandma and her grandma's dog, Shadow, on the island where her grandma lives during the summer. This is the story of how they spend their days and the special things they do together.

MacGregor, Ellen   *Miss Pickerell Goes to Mars*

While Miss Pickerell spends a month with her nieces and nephews, a rocket is built in her pasture. She climbs aboard to find out who did it and to make them remove it from her land. The rocket blasts off for Mars, and Miss Pickerell begins a fantastic journey.

Sobol, Donald J.   *Encyclopedia Brown Saves the Day*

Knowing as much as a set of encyclopedias not only helps Encyclopedia Brown solve many mysteries but also earns him his nickname. This collection of stories tells only some of the mysteries that he solves.

CHALLENGES

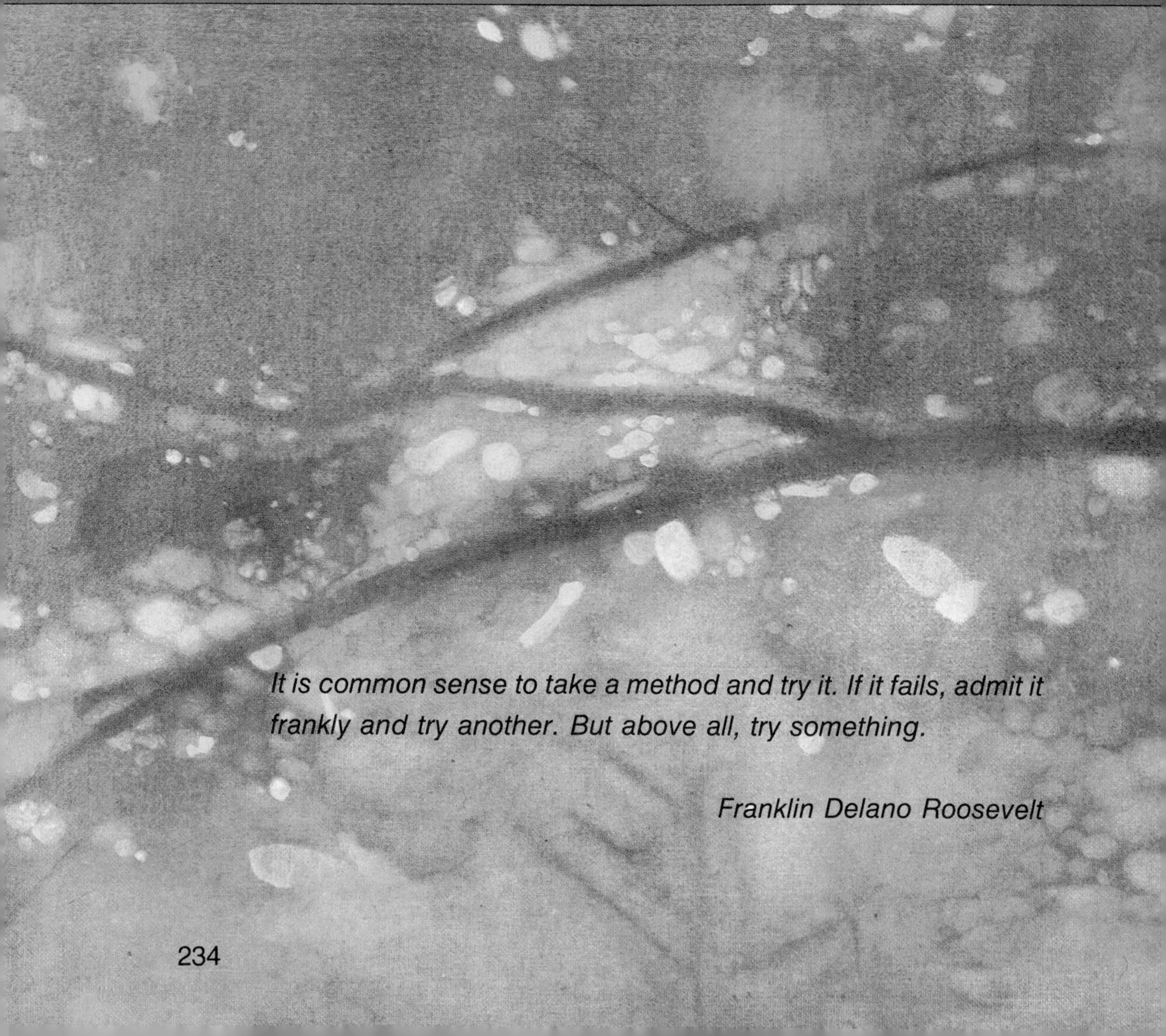

It is common sense to take a method and try it. If it fails, admit it frankly and try another. But above all, try something.

Franklin Delano Roosevelt

234

Sally Ride's Challenge

Marie Cocinero

By the time you are an adult, space travel may be an everyday thing. You may even vacation on the moon. But for just a moment, think about what it would have been like to be one of the early space explorers.

Young Sally Kristen Ride was like many other girls her age. She grew up in Los Angeles, California. She played a lot of tennis. She had fun with a sister she called "Bear." She went to church with her family. And she made good grades in school.

Most of all, Sally enjoyed reading things written by Shakespeare. She wanted to learn more about his plays and poems. Stanford University would be a good place to do this, she decided.

Sally studied more than Shakespeare at Stanford. Because she also liked science, she took courses in physics. This is the study of heat, sound, light, electricity, mechanics, and magnetism.

Another subject that had always interested Sally was astronomy. She liked to look at the sun, the moon, and the stars. They were so far away they hardly seemed real. She wanted to know more about them.

Sally found a way to learn more about the wonders of space. She put these two sciences together. Now she was able to study the universe in a different way. What were stars made of? How were they formed? How old were they? How did they move? What made them change? Sally was eager to learn everything she could.

Dr. Sally K. Ride

Then came an important day in 1977. While Sally was reading a Stanford newspaper, a story caught her eye. It said that the National Aeronautics and Space Administration needed people to train as astronauts. A background in science was essential.

Sally became excited when she read the story. She had not dreamed of such a chance. Even though she was only twenty-five, she had the right background. She knew she could do the work that the government needed.

NASA's leaders believed in Sally, too. They decided to train her. If Sally passed their tests, she might make a trip into space.

Sally would not be the first woman to do so. In 1963, the Russians decided to send a woman into space. They chose Valentina Tereshkova, a factory worker. Valentina, who had little training, became sick during her flight.

This worried the Russians. They believed that Valentina became sick only because she was a woman. A Russian leader then said that no more women could go into space.

However, the Russians learned that men could become sick, too. Doctors began studying ways to keep people well during space-flights.

In 1982 the Russians sent up another woman. Her name was Svetlana Savitskaya. This time the Russians had planned ahead. Svetlana was well trained. She even carried out several tasks during her flight. Even more important, she didn't get sick.

The United States entered the space race in the early 1960s. Everyone believed that it was a pilot's job to fly a spaceship. So, only pilots were allowed to be astronauts. All of the first ones were men.

At one time, a few women pilots were accepted. This plan never got off the ground, however. For fifteen years no more women were chosen.

During this time, many space-ships were sent up. They were safely brought down again. They were sent here and there. Finally they went around the world. One by one, many questions about flight were answered.

It was now time to begin studying space. The government started looking for scientists.

At first only men were chosen. However, the government soon discovered that many women had good backgrounds, as well. The rule about using only men was finally dropped.

How women's rights groups rejoiced! They thought it was a victory for women. But the truth was that the very *best* people were needed, men *or* women.

In 1977 more than eight thousand people asked to be astronauts. Only thirty-five were accepted. Six of these were women. Two more women were added in 1980.

The eight women were Anna Fisher, Kathryn Sullivan, Margaret Rhea Seddon, Mary Cleave, Bonnie Dunbar, Judith Resnik, Shannon Lucid, and Sally Ride. All were accustomed to hard work. Each was open to new ideas, as well.

After six years of training, Sally Ride was chosen for the *Challenger* mission. It would be the United States' seventh space-shuttle flight.

To get ready, Sally worked almost twelve hours a day, six days a week. She was trained to fly an airplane. She was taught how to stay alive if she landed in the ocean. And she learned to adapt to sudden acceleration and extreme heat and cold.

However, Sally was not always isolated from people. She had time to become friends with the other women in her group. And in 1982, she became the bride of astronaut Steven Hawley.

By June 18, 1983, more than 500,000 people had arrived at Kennedy Space Center, Florida. Dawn found them standing on beaches, looking up into the sky. They had come to see America's first woman in space.

Sally was surprised. She did not want people to think that she was more important than the other crew members. Four very able men were making the trip with her. Their names were Commander Robert Crippen, Frederick Hauck, John Fabian, and Norman Thagard.

These five people were the best to be found for the job at hand. Sally felt proud to be part of such a well-

Water survival training for Dr. Shannon W. Lucid, an astronaut candidate, begins at the top of a forty-five-foot tower to which a wire has been attached. She must slide from the tower, splash into a pool of water, release the parachute harness, swim under a parachute canopy that has been stretched over the water, and climb into a life raft.

trained group. They were going to try many new tasks in space.

The lift-off went well. The 100-ton blue and white ship flew up like a bird. Sally tried not to sound excited on the radio. But she said that her upward flight was like a trip to Disneyland.

Then it came time for everybody to go to work. The *Challenger* had to prove itself. It was like a truck that shipped things. Some of its customers were governments of other countries: Canada, Indonesia, and Germany.

Sally's most important job was to work with a long robot arm. With the arm she moved a packaged German laboratory out of the ship. Later, she reached out and caught it. Then she carefully pulled it back in again.

The group also did important work for Americans. They mixed metals that won't go together on earth. They made glass in sound waves. They started seeds to see how plants would grow. They even tried to learn whether the habits of ants would change in space.

Six days later, the ship landed. All over the world people cheered. Hundreds of news stories were written about Sally. She was asked to appear on many TV shows.

All of this attention didn't change Sally. She learned many new things, but she had a lot of fun.

Most of all, she felt proud to be a part of such an important flight.

From the flight deck of the space-shuttle *Challenger*, Dr. Sally Ride talks with ground controllers.

Challenger's crew photographed themselves during flight by using a pre-set camera. From left to right are: Norman E. Thagard, Commander Robert L. Crippen, Frederick H. Hauck, Sally K. Ride, and John M. Fabian.

Answer these questions.

1. Who was the first woman to make a trip in space? When was the trip made?

2. Why was Svetlana Savitskaya's space trip more successful than Valentina Tereshkova's?

3. Why was the acceptance of Sally Ride's application to be an astronaut such an honor?

4. How long was Sally Ride in training to become an astronaut? What kinds of things did she learn?

5. When did Sally Ride make her first space-shuttle flight into space? What was her most important job during the flight?

Write on your own.

Think of a famous person who interests you. Imagine that this person is planning to visit your school. You are a reporter for a newspaper that prints only news about your school. You have been asked to interview this person. Write a list of five questions you would ask in the interview.

Chuka's Hawk

Elizabeth B. Whitmore

Chuka is a Hopi Indian. He is the youngest member of his family, and he wants to prove that he is growing up. Chuka's grandfather often tells stories about adventures he had when he was a boy. In this story Chuka has an adventure of his own to tell about.

Chuka was playing on the roof of his house, keeping well away from the corner where Big Brother's eagle was tied. The little Hopi boy looked at the sun. Only a small piece of it was showing above the mountains. Big Brother would come soon to feed the eagle.

Chuka stopped playing and stood watching the trail that led up to the mesa from the desert below. Soon he saw Big Brother coming, his bow and arrow in his hand and his hunting bag full.

Big Brother climbed up the ladder onto the roof. His eagle pulled at the cord tied to its foot and screamed. Big Brother tossed meat to his eagle, and the eagle gulped it down.

Chuka hopped on one foot. "I want a pet eagle, too," he cried.

"Ho, you are too little." Big Brother laughed.

Mother was calling. They went down the ladder and

into the house. Mother was dishing up stew from a pot in the fireplace. She handed a bowl to Big Brother, and he went to sit beside Father and Grandfather. She handed one to Chuka. He sat near the fireplace. He dipped a piece of corn bread in the stew and ate it. Hm-m-m-m, it was good. Chuka was very, very hungry.

When they were finished, Chuka helped clear away the bowls and wash them.

Chuka brought his blankets from the storeroom and spread them on the floor. Every night Grandfather told stories about the Hopi gods or the birds and animals. Tonight Grandfather told about adventures he had had when he was a boy. Chuka liked these stories best of all.

In the morning the thump, thump of Father's loom awakened Chuka. He rolled up his blankets and took them into the storeroom. He took a piece of cold corn bread and went out to play with Grandfather's new

puppy, Bakito. When Big Brother came along, Chuka called, "Take me with you to herd the sheep in the desert, Big Brother."

"You are too little to walk so far," said Big Brother.

Chuka watched Big Brother start down the trail; then he went to see Uncle, who was working at his loom.

"You do not look happy, Chuka," said Uncle.

"I want a pet eagle," said Chuka. "Will you help me catch one?"

"An eagle cannot be tamed," said Uncle. "Your brother's eagle will never make a good pet. You can tame a hawk, if you are patient. Tomorrow we will hunt for a hawk."

The next morning Chuka and Uncle walked and walked. Finally, Chuka heard bird sounds from high in the air. He looked up. "Those are hawks," Uncle said. "We are in a good place. Look for a hawk's nest in a tree."

Uncle walked ahead, looking and looking. Chuka saw a young hawk on the lowest branch of a tree. He watched it fly to the ground, snap up a grasshopper, and then fly back to the branch again.

Chuka caught four grasshoppers in a bush. He held them in his hand while he wriggled out of his shirt. Then he threw the grasshoppers on the ground in front of the hawk. The hawk swooped down to snap them up, and Chuka threw his shirt over the bird and caught him. The hawk struggled, but Chuka held on.

When Uncle came back, he asked, "What do you have there, Chuka?"

"A young hawk!" cried Chuka.

"You caught a hawk?" Uncle was surprised.

They carried the hawk home and tied it by a cord on the housetop, as far away from Big Brother's eagle as they could. The hawk snapped its bill at the eagle.

"My hawk is not afraid of the eagle!" cried Chuka.

"Remember, you can tame him," said Uncle.

Every day Chuka went hunting. When he could shoot a mouse, he gave it to his hawk. When he couldn't, he caught grasshoppers. One day he stroked the hawk's head. It did not snap at him. After that, Chuka stroked the hawk's head whenever he fed him. The hawk liked Chuka. He rubbed his bill on Chuka's cheek and perched on Chuka's shoulder. After a while, Chuka untied the cord, climbed down the ladder, and took his hawk for a walk. The hawk perched on Chu-

ka's shoulder. He was getting tame. The boy named his pet Wiki.

It was now time for Big Brother to learn how to weave blankets. Grandfather would teach him, and Father would herd the sheep.

"Come with me, Chuka," said Father. "It is time for you to learn to herd."

Every day Father and Chuka took the sheep out into the desert. Chuka learned to find grass and water for the sheep and to keep the flock together. He missed his hawk, though. He played with Wiki a little while every evening when he fed him.

After many weeks, Father said, "Bring the young dog Bakito today. He, too, must learn to work." As soon as Bakito had learned to herd, Father said, "Chuka, I am needed in the fields to plant the squash and corn and beans. You are big enough to herd the sheep. Bakito will help you watch over them."

Chuka felt very big and brave as he went down from the mesa with only Bakito. When he was out in the desert, though, he did not feel big. He did not feel brave. The desert was hot and quiet and as empty as the sky. The day was as long as a week.

That night Chuka said to his father, "May I take Wiki with me when I go into the desert tomorrow?"

"Will you play with the hawk and forget to watch the sheep?" asked Father.

"Oh, no," said Chuka.

"Then you may take Wiki," said Father.

"Your hawk will fly away and leave you," said Big Brother.

The next morning when Chuka left the mesa, Wiki was perched on his shoulder. Every day Chuka herded the sheep, with Wiki and Bakito to help. Bakito chased rabbits and prairie dogs. Wiki found grasshoppers and snapped them up. Sometimes his sharp eyes saw a mouse, and he pounced on it. Once he heard other hawks high in the air. He left Chuka's shoulder and flew up, up until he was flying with them.

Chuka watched the hawks until he could not tell which one was Wiki. He was afraid Wiki would not come back. Soon a hawk began to fly down in big circles. When it was quite low, it swooped down and nipped Bakito on the ear. Bakito howled, but Chuka was so glad Wiki had come back that he laughed and laughed.

One day while Bakito was chasing rabbits and Wiki was playing with the other hawks high in the air, an animal chased the sheep. It looked like a dog, but Chuka knew it was a hungry coyote! It wanted a lamb to eat—one of his family's lambs!

Chuka found a big stick. He waved the stick at the coyote and shouted, but the coyote did not run away. It snarled and dashed at Chuka. He yelled and tried to hit the coyote with the stick, but it was too quick for him and dodged aside.

The sheep ran wild, baaing and bleating in panic.

"Bakito! Wiki! Help! Help!" screamed Chuka.

The hawk heard Chuka. Wiki did not sail down in big circles this time. He folded his wings and swooped down from the sky like an arrow. He dug his claws into the coyote's back and nipped and nipped. The coyote howled. It ran away. Then Wiki flew to Chuka and perched on his shoulder. He rubbed Chuka's cheek with his bill.

Chuka laughed and rubbed Wiki's head. Then Bakito rounded up the sheep. When he had them all together again, Chuka praised him and petted him.

That evening Chuka ate two bowls of beans cooked with onions and peppers for supper. He ate three big pieces of corn bread. When the dishes were cleared away, Chuka looked at Grandfather.

"Tonight *I* have a story to tell," he said.

Then Chuka told about the coyote. He told about the big stick. He told about Wiki and Bakito.

When the story was finished, Father said, "My son, you have done well. Tomorrow you may choose a lamb to have for your very own."

Big Brother went to the storeroom. He came back with his best arrow in his hand. He gave it to Chuka. "I will help you make a bigger bow," he said.

Chuka is busy. He and Wiki and Bakito drive the

sheep out into the desert every morning. They watch them all day and drive them home in the evening. They are not afraid. They know they can take good care of the sheep.

A Feather Detective

Mary Dean

Sometimes scientists work as detectives, using micro-scopes to help solve mysteries. One of these scientists is Roxie Laybourne, a bird expert who works at the National Museum of Natural History.

Roxie Laybourne has a job like no other. There's little she doesn't know about feathers.

Roxie can often tell what kind of bird a feather came from just by looking at it. If not, she studies the feather under her microscope. Soon she has the answer. This is quite a task. Why? There are about 10,000 kinds of birds.

When Roxie receives some feathers, she first washes them. Then she is ready to take a close look at each one. If she still has no answer, she goes to her books for help.

Roxie's work is important to people who build airplane engines. They sometimes find feathers in engines of downed airplanes. Are the feathers from one large bird? Are they from a flock of small birds? Roxie finds the answer so that safer engines can be built.

Roxie also studies feathers found with very old things. Perhaps a feather is found in a clay pot dug up in New Mexico. Nobody knows what

kind of feather it is. It is sent to Roxie. She says it came from a South American bird.

Who brought this feather to New Mexico hundreds of years ago? That's for someone else to decide. Roxie's job is done.

It took Roxie years to learn so much about birds. They are not simple animals at all. They are heavier than air, but still they fly. Some fly in strange ways.

A hummingbird can fly forward and backward. It can also stay in one place as it sips nectar from flowers.

A swift can fly more than 100 miles (160 kilometers) an hour for a short time. Some geese have flown as high as 29,000 feet (8,840 meters).

At times some birds fly without moving their wings. A falcon can dive at a speed of 200 miles (322 kilometers) an hour. A vulture can spread its wings and sail on the wind.

How is flight possible?

A balance between body weight and wing size is important. A bird's skeleton is light because many of its bones are hollow. Much of its body is made up of strong breast muscles.

These move the wings in a pattern like an eight. A wing is curved so that the air pressure under it is greater than that above it.

On the downstroke of a bird's wing, the feathers overlap. No air passes through. This gives the bird a strong push through the air.

It's easy for the bird to lift its wing. The wing feathers tilt like blinds on a window. Air flows through them, so the wing moves easily. This gives the bird a rest. Then it is ready to make another strong push.

Some birds can't fly at all. One of these birds is the ostrich. Even though it is large, it can run fast. Another bird that can't fly is the penguin. Its feathers are just right for swimming, however.

Even though some birds can't fly, all birds do have feathers. Some birds have as few as 900 feathers. Others may have as many as 25,000. A single bird can have more than a dozen kinds of feathers.

A six-inch feather can have 1,200 barbs. These are the featherlike shoots on the quill. Each barb can have more than 800 tiny barbules. These can't be seen by the eye alone.

Two feathers may look exactly alike. However, when Roxie puts them under a microscope, she may see many differences.

This is why Roxie is able to help the police. Once they were sure that two men had set fire to a building. It had been used to store mattress stuffing. Roxie looked at some feathers found in the men's clothing. The feathers were from turkeys, ducks, and geese. Sure enough, they were the kind of feathers that had been stored in the building.

With Roxie Laybourne on the job, nobody can get away with a *fowl* deed!

Answer these questions.

1. If Roxie Laybourne cannot identify a feather just by looking at it, what does she do?

2. How does Roxie help keep air travelers safe?

3. What puzzle was created when Roxie said that the feather found in the clay pot was a feather from South America? What kind of scientist would work to find an answer to this puzzle?

4. In what strange ways can birds fly?

5. What part of a bird's body is very light? What makes up a large part of a bird's body?

6. What would have happened to the men if the feathers in their clothing had not been turkey, duck, and goose feathers?

Reading in Health

Use your paper to complete the exercise below.

1. Look at the selection. What is the selection about?
2. Are there heads or subheads? What are they? What will each section be about?
3. Are charts, pictures, or diagrams used? What information do they give?
4. Are any words in boldface or italic type? List them.
5. Skim the material and make a list of words that are unfamiliar to you. Write the meanings of these words by using clues in the sentence or a dictionary.
6. Read the selection. List the important details.
7. In your own words write a paragraph that summarizes the information in the selection. If possible, use the words that you listed as unfamiliar or use synonyms for these words.

Food Groups				
Meat, Poultry, and Fish	Milk Products	Vegetables	Fruits	Cereals and Grains
Beef Chicken Tuna	Cheese Milk Yogurt	Beans Carrots Corn	Apples Oranges Bananas	Whole grain cereal Rye bread Brown rice

The Five Food Groups

To remain healthy, people should eat foods from each of the five food groups every day. These groups are meat, poultry, and fish; milk products; vegetables; fruits; and cereals and grains.

Minerals and Vitamins

All foods are sources of minerals and vitamins. Some provide more than others. However, each kind of food provides special things that the others do not.

Each Kind of Food Is Different

Nitrogen is important to the life of all living things. The best source of nitrogen is *protein,* a chemical compound. Meat, poultry, fish, and milk products contain protein. Milk also contains *calcium,* the material from which bones and teeth are made. All ordinary plants and most vegetables and fruits produce *carbohydrates,* which are a mixture of carbon, hydrogen, and oxygen. Carbohydrates provide the body with energy. Fruits, vegetables, and cereals and grains provide vitamins, minerals, and *fiber*. Fiber helps the body to *digest,* or process, food properly.

A healthy body must be fed a balanced diet. Good, balanced diets contain foods from each group.

CITY HALL

Nellie Burchardt

Betsy and some of her friends live in a Housing Project run by the city. One of the rules of the Project is that the people who live there cannot have pets. When Betsy and the children find a cat that is in need of a home, they go to City Hall to tell the mayor how they feel. Because Betsy is shy, being her group's leader is quite a challenge.

"Now let's all be real quiet," said Betsy when they got to City Hall. "They'll never let us see the mayor if we are noisy."

The children climbed the steps of the huge stone building. Down the long marble hall to the mayor's office they walked. The sound of their footsteps was lost in the great, high ceilings.

As they got to the mayor's office, the other children held back more and more, leaving Betsy in front.

"Excuse me," she said to the lady at the desk by the door that said MAYOR, "we'd like to see the mayor."

"Do you have an appointment?" asked the lady, looking up from her typewriter.

"No. We didn't know you had to. We have a petition for him."

The lady held out her hand. "I'll take care of it. You needn't wait," she said.

The children looked at each other. Ellen shook her head at Betsy but did not say anything.

"No," said Betsy. "We want to see the mayor in person."

"I'm sorry, but the mayor is very busy at a City Council meeting."

The children eyed each other again.

"We'll wait," said Betsy.

"I said the mayor is very busy," said the lady, beginning to sound annoyed. "You can't see him now."

"That's all right. We have lots of time," said Betsy. "We'll sit down and wait till he's not busy." She turned and led the way to a bench against the wall. The other children followed her and sat down in a row on the bench.

The lady at the desk pushed back her chair and stood

up. "Now, listen here, all of you," she said. "I told you that you *can't* wait. The mayor is too busy to have a bunch of noisy kids hanging around his office."

The lady seemed quite angry. Betsy wished the other children would not leave all the talking to her.

"We'll be very quiet. Please—we just *have* to see him," she pleaded. "It's very urgent."

She stood up but stopped when she saw a door open be-

hind the lady's back. A tall, rather stout man stood in the doorway. In the room behind him Betsy could see people walking around, talking to each other.

The lady did not see the man. She walked to the children with her arm raised, pointing at the door down the hall where they had come in.

"I said no! Now, out with you!" she said.

The man stepped forward.

"Come, come, Miss Witherspoon," he said, "that's no way to treat a group of future voters."

Miss Witherspoon spun around. "Oh—Mr. Mayor!" she gasped. "I didn't realize you were there. I'm so sorry if we disturbed you. I—I—I was just trying to get these children to leave, but they refuse to."

"Have you tried twisting their arms?" asked the mayor, with a wink at the children.

"Twisting their arms!" exclaimed Miss Witherspoon in a horrified voice. Then she giggled. "Oh—you're joking again. I just never know when you're joking."

"I'm glad you didn't get them to leave," continued the mayor. "It's not every day that I get a chance to talk to a group of my younger constituents."

The children looked at each other.

"Now don't tell me that you didn't know you were my constituents," said the mayor.

The children shook their heads.

"Well, don't let it worry you. It just means you're the people I represent. You know what that means, don't you?"

The children nodded their heads.

"Now," said the mayor, "out with it. To what do I owe the honor of this visit?"

Ellen gave Betsy a shove, and Betsy had to take a step forward to keep from falling.

"Yes?" said the mayor.

When he looked at her, her stomach felt shaky. He had not seemed so big in the picture she had seen in the paper.

"We—we—we have a petition here for you, M-Mr. Mayor," said Betsy. She was surprised to hear how little and shaky her voice sounded. She handed him the papers covered with signatures.

The mayor took the papers from Betsy with one hand, and with the other he reached into his pocket and pulled out his glasses. He put them on and read the petition, then turned the pages of signatures one by one and examined them carefully.

Finally he looked up at Betsy and said, "So I can have a pet and you can't, is that it?"

"Yes, sir," said Betsy in a tiny voice.

"You don't think that's fair, eh?"

"N-n-no, sir."

"What kind of pet would you get if you could have one?"

Betsy took a deep breath. "A cat. You see, there's this poor little cat that has a hurt paw—"

Suddenly the other children found their voices and all started speaking at once.

"—and we've been feeding her—"

"—and she's going to have kittens—"

"—but we're not allowed to have pets—"

"—and the weather's getting too cold—"

"Whoa! Whoa!" shouted the mayor over the babble of voices. "One at a time!"

The children fell silent.

Now that he could make himself heard, the mayor looked right at Betsy and said, "This seems to be something of an emergency. Is that it?"

"Yes, sir," said Betsy. "She's going to have her kittens any day now. Ellen's mother says if she has them outside she'll hide them somewhere and we won't be able to find them before winter comes."

"What do you say to that, Miss Witherspoon?" asked the mayor. "Kittens all over the place!"

Miss Witherspoon looked up from her desk, where she had gone back to her typing.

"Pardon me, sir?" she asked.

The mayor raised his voice. "I said we're going to have kittens all over the Project. Are we going to allow that?"

"Oh—no, sir," gasped Miss Witherspoon.

"You're right!" said the mayor. "Kittens all over the Project, scaring away the birds and digging up the flower beds. We certainly can't have that!"

Betsy's heart sank. Maybe they should not have come. The mayor had seemed so nice at first.

"You know what I'd like to do?" the mayor asked.

"N-no, sir." Betsy's voice was small and scared.

"I'd *like* you children to take those kittens in and give them homes."

Betsy gave a sigh of relief. He was nice, after all!

"*But,*" continued the mayor, "there's only one catch."

"What's that?" asked Betsy.

"I don't make the rules. The City Council has to approve any change in the rules for the Project. You know, you're not the first ones to have said the rule against pets was not fair. Now—what could we do about it?"

The children watched his face.

"Hm-m-m—yes. It just might work," he said at last. He looked at Betsy. "What's your name, little girl?"

"Who? Me?" Betsy looked around, hoping he meant some other child.

"Yes—you."

"Oh. Betsy."

"All right, Betsy. Do you think you could go in there to the City Council meeting and show them the petition just the way you showed it to me?"

"Oh—no!" Betsy stepped back toward the protection of the rest of the group. "I'd be too scared."

"You weren't too scared of me, were you, Betsy?"

"No-o-o." She remembered she *had* been afraid of him. That seemed a little silly now. He was not in the least bit mean or grumpy.

"Do you want to keep that cat, Betsy?" he asked.

"Oh—yes! I do!"

She bit her lip. That cat was making her do a lot of things she would have been too scared to do last year— talking back to Ellen, ringing all those strange doorbells to get signatures, talking to the mayor. Now he wanted her to face the City Council! Well, she'd come this far. She couldn't give it up now.

"All right. I *guess* I could do it," she said.

"That's the girl!" exclaimed the mayor.

As Betsy and the mayor entered the room, the council members went back to their seats. Betsy almost changed her mind when she saw all those strange grown-up faces looking at her from around the big council-room table. The council members looked like the kind of people who could say no to almost anything.

The mayor sat down in the chair at the head of the table and told her to stand beside him. He picked up a little wooden mallet and rapped on the table for quiet.

"I'd like to make a change in business," he said. "I want to introduce someone to you. Her name is Betsy—uh—Betsy, what's your last name?"

"Delaney."

"Her name is Betsy Delaney, and she has a problem for you."

Betsy felt a little braver. She tried not to think of all those grown-up eyes looking at her. She tried to think instead of the cat's green-and-gold eyes.

Once she started talking, it was not as hard as she had thought it would be to tell about the petition and the lame cat the children had been feeding. When she had finished and had passed around the petition for all of them to look at, the mayor whispered in her ear, "This isn't a promise, Betsy, but if I were you, I'd go home and catch that cat and lock her up before she starts having kittens all over the place."

Betsy grinned. "Oh, yes, sir!" she said.

As she turned to leave, she saw the mayor wink at her. She winked back. It seemed silly now that she had been so scared of him at first.

I'm as bad as the cat, she thought. I get scared of things before I know if there's really anything to be scared of.

She was not sure, but she thought that two of the council members were smiling. She was not quite brave enough yet to look right at all those strange grown-up faces. However, she *had* gotten them to look at the petition. That was the main thing.

Answer these questions.

1. Whom did Betsy and the other children go to see at City Hall? Why?

2. What was the rule about having pets in the Housing Project?

3. Why did the children want to keep the cat as a pet?

4. Why was Miss Witherspoon so unfriendly to the children until the mayor joked with her?

5. How did the mayor help Betsy and the others?

6. What did the mayor say to Betsy after she talked to the City Council?

Write on your own.

Betsy and the other children write a petition to explain why they think the no-pet rule is unfair. Then they ask people who agree with them to sign the petition. Pretend that you are a member of their group and that you are asked to write the petition. Write three reasons that explain why the rule should be changed.

Cities and Government

Patricia Takamura

Cities are more than just places where many people live. Cities have needs, and they have leaders to make sure that these needs are met. This article tells how cities are run.

Early cities were sometimes like small countries. The army of Athens, Greece, was very famous. The city of Venice, in Italy, had one of the world's greatest navies. These armies and navies made sure that everyone in the city was kept safe from outside enemies.

People of early cities needed to be protected from thieves. City businesses needed to work smoothly. Businesses sold the food, clothes, and other things that the people needed to live. Streets needed to be built and kept in good order by the cities since these goods were carried over streets.

Water was very important to the city. People in Rome, Italy, drank water that had been brought from hundreds of miles away. Roman leaders had huge systems built to make sure that everyone had enough water.

All of these cities had leaders. The leaders made sure that everything ran smoothly in the city. Some of the cities had kings or queens who were the leaders. Cities in America today are ruled by leaders who are chosen by the people.

Some cities have mayor-council governments.

One of the most widely used kinds of city government is the mayor-council government. The *mayor* and the people in the *city council* are elected by the people. The council members make the laws. The mayor makes sure that the laws are carried out. Together these people keep the city running smoothly.

Some cities have council-manager governments.

Another widely used form of city government is the council-manager government. The city council makes the laws. The *city manager* does the job that a mayor might do in another city. City managers are not elected. They are hired by the city council. They may be replaced at any time.

Some cities have a mayor and a city manager. The mayor is the leader of the city council. The city manager does the same job in both kinds of government.

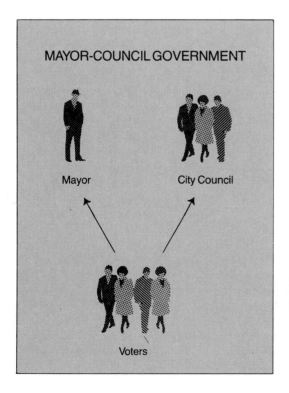

MAYOR-COUNCIL GOVERNMENT

Mayor   City Council

Voters

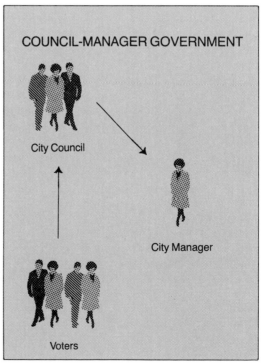

COUNCIL-MANAGER GOVERNMENT

City Council

City Manager

Voters

Some cities have commission governments.

A third kind of city government is run by a *commission*. People elected as commissioners are in charge of different departments. One may be in charge of the police. Another may run the city's water works. A third may be in charge of the city's parks. They work together to make laws. Some cities with this kind of government may also have mayors. These mayors lead the meetings of city governments.

All cities provide services.

A city government's most important job is to make sure that city services run smoothly. Some of the services are run by police, fire, garbage, park, and water departments. These services are paid for with tax money. The people who live in the city pay the taxes. The city government decides how much the taxes should be.

City governments try to make cities nice places in which to live. City governments have big jobs to do. By working with the people in the city, city governments get these jobs done.

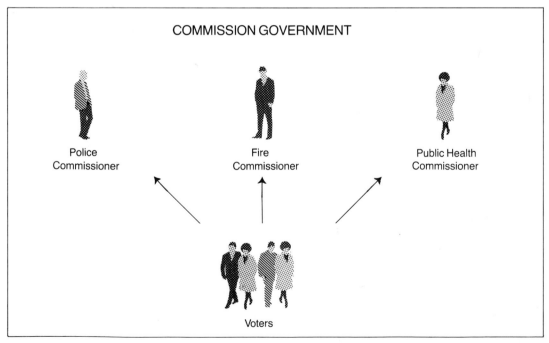

COMMISSION GOVERNMENT

Police Commissioner

Fire Commissioner

Public Health Commissioner

Voters

Answer these questions.

1. Why did some early cities have armies and navies? Who does this job in today's cities?

2. What are the three kinds of city government? How are these governments like the leaders of early cities?

3. How are mayors and city managers chosen to do their jobs?

4. Who makes the laws in each of the three kinds of city government?

5. What is the most important job of a city government?

6. Who decides which form of government a city will have?

Reading Math Word Problems

To answer a word or story problem, first read the problem carefully. Then several things must be decided before the answer can be found.

What does the reader need to find out in order to solve the problem?
The last sentence usually gives instructions or asks a question. The sentence tells what the reader will need to find as the answer to the problem.

What information does the last sentence say to use in solving the problem?
Look for words in the problem that are similar to the words used in the last sentence. For example, the last sentence may ask how many apples three people sold. The reader would need to look at other sentences in the problem to find how many apples each person sold.

What information in the problem is not needed?
Often extra facts are included in the problem. These facts may not be needed in finding the answer.

Decide whether addition, subtraction, multiplication, or division will be used in solving the problem.
If the last sentence asks:
How many are there all together? Use addition or multiplication.
How many are left? Use subtraction.
How many will each one have? Use division.

Add, subtract, multiply, or divide to find the answer to the problem.

Read the word problems below. Numbered questions follow each problem. On your paper write the answer to each numbered question.

There are twelve months in a year. One year has four seasons. How many months are in each season?

1. *In this problem, what are you supposed to find?*

Katie's mother bought thirty apples for Katie, Sue, and Debbie. It was time for the school party. How many apples did each girl give out at the party?

2. *What information will the reader need to use in solving the problem?*

There are 950 seats in the theatre. The movie is *The Purple Creature from Beyond.* 530 seats were sold. Find the number of seats that will be empty.

3. *What information in the problem is not needed?*

Jack works eight hours a day. He works five days a week. How many hours does he work in a week?

4. *Will addition, subtraction, multiplication, or division be used in finding the answer to this problem?*

Alice in Wonderland

Lewis Carroll
(Adapted by Rochelle Hill)

Alice meets a rabbit who says that he is very late. She follows him and finds herself in a wonderland full of funny characters and strange events. In this play, Alice's challenge is to decide what will happen next, what is real, and what has been dreamed.

Reprinted by permission from *Plays, The Drama Magazine for Young People*. Copyright © 1967, 1972, 1977 by Plays, Inc. This play is for reading purposes only. For permission to perform this play, write to Plays, Inc., 8 Arlington Street, Boston, Massachusetts 02116.

Characters

ALICE
WHITE RABBIT
CATERPILLAR
DUCHESS
CHESHIRE CAT
MAD HATTER
MARCH HARE
DORMOUSE
QUEEN OF HEARTS
MOCK TURTLE
ALICE'S MOTHER, *offstage voice*

BEFORE RISE: *Soft music is heard, as* ALICE *enters left, in front of curtain, book in hand. She crosses right, sits on ground.*

ALICE: I think I'll just sit here awhile and read. *(Starts reading, begins to yawn.)* Dear me, I'm getting so sleepy. *(Continues reading, but shortly her head begins to nod, and she drops book, then stretches out on ground and falls asleep.* WHITE RABBIT *hops in right, as music stops.)*

RABBIT *(Looking at his large pocket watch):* I'm late, I'm late! *(*ALICE *wakes with a start, sits up.)* Oh, dear! I'm very late!

ALICE *(Rubbing her eyes in amazement):* A rabbit!

RABBIT *(Rushing past* ALICE*):* Out of my way, girl. I'm very late.

ALICE: Late for *what*, Mr. Rabbit?

RABBIT: No time to visit, my dear—she'll *behead* me for sure.

ALICE *(Alarmed):* Who'll behead you?

RABBIT *(Excitedly):* The Queen of Hearts, the jury, *everyone!* Oh, my ears and whiskers! What a terrible fate—a rabbit without his head! I'd surely look undignified.

ALICE: Mr. Rabbit, do tell me what is wrong! *(He ignores her and exits through the curtain. She calls after him.)* Mr. Rabbit, Mr. Rabbit! Come back! There he goes down that rabbit hole. *(She gets up, follows him through the curtain. After a moment, curtain opens.)*

SETTING: *A strange garden filled with flowers of extraordinary size and color. There is a large rock up right, which hides an exit.*

AT RISE: ALICE *is sitting on ground.* CATERPILLAR *is lying on the rocks up right.* ALICE *does not see him at first.*

ALICE *(Bewildered):* Why, I must have fallen down the rabbit hole! I wonder how many miles it was. . . . It seemed I was falling right *through* the earth! And it was so dark. *(Look-*

ing around) It seems I've hit the bottom, and it didn't hurt a bit! I'm not on the other side of the earth at all, but in someone's garden. (RABBIT *rushes in right.)*

RABBIT: I'm late.

ALICE: Why, Mr. Rabbit, what are *you* doing here?

RABBIT: *I* live here. And what, may I ask, are *you* doing in my garden?

ALICE: I seem to have fallen down your rabbit hole.

RABBIT: Yes, and through my house, and now you're trampling on my garden. Such a clumsy girl. You'd best fix yourself up and hurry along or you'll be late, too. *(He starts off left.)* Oh, dear, now I'm later than ever! *(He exits in a fluster.)*

ALICE *(Shouting after him)*: Late for *what?* I just arrived! Mr. Rabbit, please come back! *(She gets up, starts after him, then stops.)* Mr. Rabbit! *(Angrily)* How rude of him! I asked him a civil question, and he deliberately ran off without giving me an answer!

CATERPILLAR *(Still calmly lying on rocks)*: Who are *you?*

ALICE *(Startled, turning around)*: I—I hardly know, sir, just at present. At least I know who I was when I got up this morning, but I think things must have changed many times since then. *(Walks over to him.)*

CATERPILLAR: What do you mean by that? Explain yourself.

ALICE: I can't explain *myself,* I'm afraid, sir, because I'm not myself.

CATERPILLAR: I don't understand.

ALICE: This morning, I was just a girl sitting by the river bank, and now I'm lost in this odd place.

CATERPILLAR: I don't find this place a bit odd.

ALICE: Well, your feelings may be different. All I know is, it seems very odd to *me!*

CATERPILLAR: You! Who are *you?*

ALICE *(Becoming irritated)*: I think you ought to tell me who *you* are first.

CATERPILLAR: Why?

ALICE *(Frustrated)*: Oh! *(She stamps her foot and starts off.)*

CATERPILLAR: Come back! I've something important to say!

ALICE *(Turning to him)*: Yes?

CATERPILLAR *(Leaning forward, his nose practically touching hers)*: Keep your temper.

ALICE: Is that all?

CATERPILLAR: No. You have no business standing in the Duchess's kitchen. (ALICE *looks around her, then becomes angry again.*)

ALICE: I'm *not* in the Duchess's kitchen! (*As* ALICE *argues with* CATERPILLAR, DUCHESS *and grinning* CHESHIRE CAT *enter left. They carry in table, large soup pot, spoon, and pepper.* DUCHESS *sits on ground beside table.*) I am standing in the White Rabbit's garden—wherever *that* is! There is no house here, and you can't have a kitchen without a house around it. And I don't know any duchess anyway!

CATERPILLAR: You certainly are standing in her kitchen. I must say you are very rude to barge into the Duchess's home without knocking.

ALICE: The Duchess! *Who* is *she?*

CATERPILLAR: *Who* are *you? (He disappears behind rocks and exits.)*

ALICE: Well, really! *(She begins sneezing.)* I certainly don't *(Sneezes)* understand him at all! *(She sneezes, then turns around to find herself standing before* DUCHESS.*)* Oh! My goodness! You must be the Duchess!

DUCHESS: Yes, and what do *you* have to say?

ALICE: Uh . . . uh . . . there's certainly too much pepper in that soup! Ach-oo!

DUCHESS: Nonsense. There's not nearly enough pepper in that soup. *(Shakes more into soup.)* Ach-oo! Not . . . ach-oo! . . . nearly enough.

ALICE *(Noticing* CHESHIRE CAT*):* Please, would you tell me why your cat grins like that?

DUCHESS: It's a Cheshire cat, and that's why.

ALICE: I didn't know that Cheshire cats always grinned. In fact, I didn't know that cats *could* grin.

DUCHESS: They all can, and most of them do.

ALICE: What sort of people live about here?

CAT: In that direction *(Waving to right)*, lives a Hatter; and in that direction *(Waving to left)*, lives a March Hare. Visit either you like. They're both mad.

ALICE: But I don't want to visit *mad* people!

CAT: Oh, you can't help that. We're all mad here. I'm mad. You're mad.

ALICE: How do you know I'm mad?

CAT: You must be, or you wouldn't have come here.

ALICE: And how do you know that you're mad?

CAT: To begin with, a dog's not mad. You grant that?

ALICE: I suppose so.

CAT: Well, then, a dog growls when it's angry, and wags its tail when it's pleased. Now, *I* growl when I'm pleased, and wag my tail when I'm angry. Therefore, I'm mad.

ALICE: *I* call it purring, not growling.

CAT: Call it what you like. *(Pause)* Do you plan to play croquet with the Queen today?

ALICE: I suppose I should like it very much, but I haven't been invited.

CAT: You'll see me there. *(There is a pause. ALICE turns to leave.)*

ALICE: Goodbye. *(CAT disappears slowly behind rock and exits. Singing and laughter are heard, then MAD HATTER, MARCH HARE, and DORMOUSE enter. They are carrying tea cups, teapot, etc., with which they set table. ALICE turns to watch them, then speaks to herself.)* Well, I certainly didn't have to go far at all. It's just as well. I'm not sure the cat's directions were very precise anyway. *(MAD HATTER and MARCH HARE sit at either side of sleeping DORMOUSE with their elbows resting on him. They see ALICE coming and begin shouting.)*

HATTER *and* HARE: No room! No room!

ALICE *(Indignantly)*: There's *plenty* of room! *(She sits at the table.)*

HARE: It wasn't very civil of you to sit down without being invited.

ALICE: I didn't know it was *your* table—it's set for a great many more than three.

HATTER: Why is a raven like a writing desk?

ALICE: Oh, a riddle! I believe I can guess that.

HARE: Do you mean you think you can find the answer to it?

ALICE: Exactly so.

HARE: Then you should say what you mean.

ALICE: I do. At least—at least I mean what I say—that's the same thing, you know.

HATTER: Not the same thing a bit! Why, you might just as well say that "I see what I eat" is the same thing as "I eat what I see."

HARE: You might just as well say that "I like what I get" is the same thing as "I get what I like."

DORMOUSE *(Talking in his sleep):* You might just as well say that "I breathe when I sleep" is the same thing as "I sleep when I breathe."

HATTER *(To* DORMOUSE*):* It *is* the same thing with you! *(*HATTER *and* HARE *drink their tea.* HATTER *takes his watch out of his pocket, shakes it several times, and holds it to his ear.)* What day of the month is it?

ALICE: The fourth.

HATTER: Two days wrong! *(To* HARE*)* I told you the butter wouldn't suit the works.

HARE: It was the *best* butter.

HATTER: Yes, but some crumbs must have fallen in as well. You shouldn't have put it in with the bread knife. *(*HARE *takes watch, shakes it, dips it into his tea, then puts it down.)*

HARE: It was the *best* butter, you know.

ALICE *(Looking at watch):* What a funny watch! It tells the day of the month, and doesn't tell what o'clock it is!

HATTER: Why should it? Does *your* watch tell you what year it is?

ALICE: Of course not, but that's because it stays the same year for such a long time.

HATTER: Which is just the case with *mine.*

ALICE *(Puzzled):* I don't quite understand you.

HATTER: The Dormouse is asleep again. *(He pretends to pour tea on* DORMOUSE'S *nose.)*

DORMOUSE *(Talking in his sleep):* Of course, of course, just what I was going to say myself.

HATTER *(To* ALICE*):* Have you guessed the riddle yet?

ALICE: No, I give up. What's the answer?

HATTER: I haven't the slightest idea.

ALICE *(Exasperated):* I think you might do something better with the time than wasting it in asking riddles that have no answers.

HATTER: If you knew Time as well as I do, you wouldn't talk about wasting *it*. It's *him!*

ALICE: I don't know what you mean.

HATTER: Of course not! I dare say you've never even spoken to Time!

ALICE: Perhaps not.

HATTER: If you only keep on good terms with him, he'll do almost anything you like with the clock. For instance, suppose it were nine o'clock in the morning, just in time to begin lessons; you'd only have to whisper a hint to Time, and round goes the clock in a twinkling! Half past one, time for dinner!

HARE *(To himself):* I only wish it were.

ALICE: That would be grand, certainly, but then—I shouldn't be hungry for it, you know.

HATTER: Not at first, perhaps, but you could keep it to half past one as long as you liked.

ALICE: Is that the way *you* manage?

HATTER *(Sadly):* Not I. We quarreled last March—just before *he* (Pointing to HARE) went mad, you know. It was at the great concert given by the Queen of Hearts, and I had to sing. *(Singing)*

Twinkle, Twinkle, little bat!

How I wonder where you're at!

You know the song, perhaps?

ALICE: I've heard something like it.

HATTER: It goes on, you know, in this way. *(Singing)*
  Up above the world you fly,
  Like a teatray in the sky,
  Twinkle, twinkle—

DORMOUSE *(Singing in his sleep):* Twinkle, twinkle, twinkle, . . . *(He stops when* HATTER *and* HARE *poke him.)*

HATTER: Well, I'd hardly finished the first verse when the Queen bawled out, "He's murdering the time! Off with his head!"

ALICE: How dreadfully savage!

HATTER: And ever since then, Time won't do a thing I ask! It's always six o'clock now.

ALICE: Is *that* the reason so many tea things are put out here?

HATTER *(Sighing):* Yes, that's it. It's always teatime, and we've no time to wash the things between whiles.

ALICE: Then you keep moving round, I suppose.

HATTER: Exactly so, as the cups get used up.

ALICE: But when do you come to the beginning again?

HARE: There is no beginning.

ALICE: Of course there is! Everything must have a beginning!

HARE: Exactly so. The beginning already began, so the beginning is used up and now there is no beginning.

ALICE: Then what do you do when you come to the end?

HATTER: There is no end until it finishes, and it's always six o'clock, so we haven't gotten there yet.

ALICE: Then what do you do when you're in the *middle?*

HARE: Drink tea. Have some more.

ALICE: I've had nothing yet, so I can't take more.

HATTER: You mean you can't take less. It's very easy to take *more* than nothing.

ALICE: Nobody asked *your* opinion.

HATTER: Now you're making personal remarks!

DORMOUSE: Twinkle, twinkle, twinkle—

ALICE (*Stamping her foot*): Oh! (*She walks away left in disgust, then turns back, but they are busy trying to keep* DORMOUSE *from singing.*) At any rate, I'll never go *there* again! It's the stupidest tea party I was ever at in all my life! (*Goes and sulks downstage left.*)

HARE: My cup is dirty. Everyone move to the next place.

HATTER: Move the other way! We've moved this way three times already.

DORMOUSE: Twinkle, twinkle, twinkle, twinkle—

HARE: Put the Dormouse in the teapot and I'll sit at his place.

HATTER: But his things are slept on! It's much better to drink

from a dirty cup than one that's been slept on. *(HATTER stops talking, when croquet players—RABBIT, CATERPILLAR, DUCHESS, CAT, and QUEEN OF HEARTS—enter left, carrying mallets and hitting their balls ahead of them. They are yelling at each other. RABBIT hits croquet ball, which rolls to HATTER, who picks it up.)*

QUEEN OF HEARTS: Off with your head.

RABBIT: Who has my ball? Oh, my ears and whiskers, I shall never be able to play without my ball!

HATTER: I believe I have it. Care to join us for tea?

CATERPILLAR *(To HATTER):* Who are *you?*

QUEEN *(Seeing HATTER with ball):* Off with his head! *(At this, HATTER and HARE run out right with their table and tea things. DORMOUSE is left behind, asleep. Croquet game continues without organization.)* Whose turn is it?

DUCHESS: Mine.

QUEEN: Off with your head! (HARE *and* HATTER *run back in, unnoticed by players, and carry* DORMOUSE *off.* QUEEN *notices* ALICE, *who has been dodging balls and people all this time.)* Who are you?

ALICE *(Startled, curtsying):* My name is Alice, Your Majesty.

QUEEN *(Shouting as usual):* Can you play croquet?

ALICE *(Shouting back):* Yes!

QUEEN: Then play! Or off with your head!

ALICE: If you please, Your Majesty, I don't have a mallet or a ball. If you would be so kind as to—*(As she speaks, they all exit right, hitting their balls offstage as they go.* ALICE *is left alone on stage.)* Oh, well, at least I still have my head, and that's something to be grateful for! They're dreadfully fond of beheading people here. It's a great wonder that there's anyone left alive! *(*RABBIT *enters, scroll in hand.)*

RABBIT: The trial's beginning! Hear ye! The trial's beginning! *(Pointing to left)* The jury sits here. *(*RABBIT *is followed by* CATERPILLAR, DUCHESS, *carrying pepper shaker,* CAT, HATTER, *carrying teacup,* HARE, *and* DORMOUSE. *Each carries slate and chalk.* TURTLE *joins jury.)*

ALICE *(To* RABBIT, *who is running around nervously):* What trial is this? *(He ignores her. All attention is drawn to* QUEEN'S *entrance right. She takes her place at center.* ALICE *notices jury members writing on their slates.)* What are they doing? They can't have anything to write down before the trial begins.

RABBIT: They're putting down their names, for fear they will forget them before the end of the trial.

ALICE *(Quite loudly):* Stupid things!

QUEEN: Silence in the court! Herald, read the accusation.

RABBIT *(Unrolling his scroll):*

    The Queen of Hearts, she made some tarts,

    All on a summer day;

    The Knave of Hearts, he stole these tarts,

    And took them quite away!

QUEEN: Consider the verdict!

RABBIT: Not yet, not yet! There's a great deal to come before that.

QUEEN: Call the first witness.

RABBIT: Mad Hatter!

HATTER *(Stepping forward, teacup in hand):* I beg your pardon, Your Majesty, for bringing my tea in, but I hadn't quite finished my tea when I was sent for.

QUEEN: You ought to have finished. When did you begin?

HATTER: Fourteenth of March, I *think* it was.

HARE: Fifteenth.

DORMOUSE: Sixteenth.

QUEEN *(To jury):* Write that down. *(To* HATTER*):* Take off that hat.

HATTER: It isn't mine.

QUEEN: Stolen!

HATTER *(Becoming nervous):* I keep them to sell. I've none of my own. I'm a Hatter.

QUEEN: Give your evidence and don't be nervous, or I'll have you executed.

HATTER: I'm a poor man, Your Majesty, and I had just begun my tea, when the March Hare said—

HARE: I didn't!

HATTER: You did!

HARE: I deny it!

QUEEN: He denies it—leave that part out.

HATTER: Well, at any rate, the Dormouse said—um—and then I cut some more bread and butter—

CATERPILLAR: What did the Dormouse say?

HATTER: That I can't remember.

QUEEN: You *must* remember or I'll have you executed.

ALICE: That's not fair!

QUEEN: *Silence!* Or off with *your* head. (ALICE *steps back.* QUEEN *turns to* HATTER.) If that's all you know about it you may stand down.

HATTER: I'd rather finish my tea. (QUEEN *glares at him, and he sits down with jury.*)

QUEEN: Call the next witness!

RABBIT: Duchess! (*She steps forward with pepper shaker in her hand.*)

QUEEN: Give your evidence.

DUCHESS: Shan't.

QUEEN (*Shouting with anger*): What are tarts made of?

DUCHESS: Pepper, mostly.

DORMOUSE (*Sleepily*): Tea!

QUEEN: Collar that Dormouse! Behead him! Pinch him! Off with his whiskers! (*He promptly falls asleep.*) Never mind. Call the next witness.

RABBIT: Alice!

ALICE (*Stepping forward*): Yes?

QUEEN: What do you know of this business?

ALICE: Nothing.

QUEEN: Nothing *whatever?*

ALICE: Nothing whatever.

QUEEN (*To jury*): Consider your verdict.

ALICE: You can't consider the verdict yet. You haven't the proper evidence.

RABBIT: Of course we have. The jury has it all written down.

ALICE: If any one of them can explain the evidence, I'll give them a sixpence. *I* don't believe there's an atom of meaning in it!

QUEEN: If there's no meaning in it, that saves a world of trouble. We needn't try to find any.

CAT: Consider the verdict!

QUEEN: No, no! Sentence first—verdict afterward.

ALICE: Stuff and nonsense! The idea of having the sentence first!

QUEEN: *Off with her head!*

ALICE: Who cares for you? You're nothing but a pack of cards!

ALL *(Standing and pointing at* ALICE*)*: Guilty! *You* stole the tarts! Off with her head! Silly creatures indeed! *(Etc.)*

(Their voices grow louder and louder. Alice *backs away from them to edge of stage, sits and falls asleep, as curtain closes behind her. Voices stop abruptly. There is silence, then* Alice's Mother *is heard calling from off left.)*

Mother *(Off left):* Alice! Alice, where are you?

Alice *(Awakening):* Oh, what a curious dream I've just had.

Mother *(Off left):* Alice!

Alice *(Calling off left):* Coming, Mother! *(To herself, still quite sleepy and puzzled)* It all began when the White Rabbit ran across the bank—right over here—and he was so worried about being late. And I followed him—*(She looks around, as if trying to remember.)* I followed him over *here.* *(She goes center of curtain, but cannot find the opening.)* At least I *thought* there was a rabbit hole here—and somehow I fell down it ever so far and found myself among curious creatures in a strange land—a *wonder-*land! *(She runs off left, as soft music plays again.)*

About the Author

Lewis Carroll was an author and a math teacher in England during the last half of the 1800s. He liked children very much and would often amuse the children of his friends by making up stories for them. He wrote *Alice's Adventures in Wonderland* for Alice Liddell, the daughter of the dean of the school where Carroll taught math.

Answer these questions.

1. What was the White Rabbit doing and saying when Alice woke up?

2. Where did Alice go when she followed the Rabbit?

3. How did Alice answer the Caterpillar when he asked who she was?

4. What problem did the Mad Hatter have with his watch and with time itself?

5. For what crime did the Queen of Hearts order a trial? What made the Queen say that Alice was guilty of the crime?

6. Was Alice sure that everything that happened was real? How do you know?

FLOWER CHORUS

Oh, such a commotion under the ground
When March called 'Ho, there! ho!'
Such spreading of rootlets far and wide,
Such whisperings to and fro!
'Are you ready?' the Snowdrop asked,
''Tis time to start, you know.'
'Almost, my dear!' the Scilla replied,
'I'll follow as soon as you go.'
Then 'Ha! ha! ha!' a chorus came
Of laughter sweet and low
Of millions of flowers under the ground,
Yes, millions, beginning to grow.

'I'll promise my blossoms,' the Crocus said
'When I hear the blackbird sing.'
'And straight thereafter,' Narcissus cried,
'My silver and gold I'll bring.'
'And ere they are dulled,' another spoke,
'The hyacinth bells shall ring.'
But the Violet only murmured 'I'm here,'
And sweet grew the air of the spring.
Then 'Ha! ha! ha!' a chorus came
Of laughter sweet and low
Of millions of flowers under the ground,
Yes, millions, beginning to grow.

Ralph Waldo Emerson

About the Author

A philosopher and an author, Ralph Waldo Emerson grew up in New England in the early 1800s. He was often sick as a child, and his family was very poor. As a young man, he went to Europe and met many of the leading philosophers and writers of his day. These people's thoughts were great influences upon his own ideas.

Reading in Social Studies

Use your paper to complete the exercise below.

1. Look at the selection. What is the selection about?
2. Are there heads or subheads? What are they? What will each section be about?
3. Are any words in boldface or italic type? List them.
4. Skim the material and make a list of words that are unfamiliar to you. Write the meanings of these words by using clues in the sentence or a dictionary.
5. Read the selection. List the important details.
6. In your own words write a paragraph that summarizes the information in the selection. If possible, use the words that you listed as unfamiliar or use synonyms for these words.

The Vikings

Who Were the Vikings?

The Vikings were a Scandinavian people who lived in northern Europe. They lived in mountainous regions. Because the Vikings did not have much good land, they turned to the sea for food, transportation, and trade. They learned to be the best sailors of their time. Their ships, long rowing boats with sails, were among the best and fastest in Europe.

How Did the Vikings Sail?

The Vikings sailed all over without compasses or modern instruments. Experience had taught them many things. By watching the flight of birds, sailors could tell where land was. The Vikings also used the sun and stars to help them sail from east to west in a straight line. They kept records of the sun's path across the sky. By measuring the angle from the ship to the sun at noon, sailors could tell whether they were too far north or south of their course. Sunrise and sunset showed where east and west were. At night, the North Star was their guide. The North Star, or *polestar,* is a star toward which the earth's North Pole points. Therefore, it shows where north is. The Vikings made maps to share their knowledge.

Vocabulary Review

On your paper write **a, b, c,** or **d** to show the item that best completes the sentence.

1. To miss an appointment is to miss attending a _____.
   - a. scheduled meeting
   - b. good time
   - c. late arrival
   - d. new plan

2. Cloth is made on a loom, the machine used in _____.
   - a. plowing
   - b. weeping
   - c. keeping
   - d. weaving

3. Something is isolated if it has been set _____.
   - a. apart
   - b. upon
   - c. around
   - d. down

4. Things that hold nothing are hollow, or _____.
   - a. thick
   - b. empty
   - c. small
   - d. embarrassed

5. Special things are rare, extraordinary, or _____.
   - a. older
   - b. large
   - c. unusual
   - d. uninteresting

6. Something irritating may be a commotion, or _____.
   - a. disturbance
   - b. engine
   - c. party
   - d. disbelief

7. For good health, vitamins are essential, or _____.
   - a. wasted
   - b. necessary
   - c. needless
   - d. beautiful

Books to Read

Carroll, Lewis   *Alice's Adventures in Wonderland*
A white rabbit who is late for a very important date leads Alice down his rabbit hole and into a very special place. This is the story of what Alice finds and of her adventures in Wonderland.

Kjelgaard, Jim   *Big Red*
A champion Irish setter blends naturally into life in the woods with Danny and his father. He even manages to help them catch the bear that has been killing livestock.

Monjo, F. N.   *Grand Papa and Ellen Aroon*
Thomas Jefferson was the third president of the United States. This biography of Jefferson is told as if written by his granddaughter Ellen Aroon.

Mowat, Farley   *Owls in the Family*
Billy and his family get two new pets. However, the new pets are owls. This family's life changes greatly with these two animals as new members of the household.

Wheeler, Opal   *Ludwig Beethoven and the Chiming Tower Bells*
Even though he lost his hearing, Ludwig van Beethoven continued to write and conduct some of the world's greatest music. Opal Wheeler tells the story of his life.

WONDERS

In all things of nature there is something of the marvelous.

Aristotle

307

snow. Daniel could tell from the size of the tracks that it was a young hare.

He walked out of the swamp and started down the mountain toward the river. Here the trees were all hardwoods. The sun shone brightly through the bare branches. A chickadee scolded Daniel from a nearby tree.

Daniel saw tiny ruffed grouse tracks everywhere. These birds had come to eat the buds off birch trees. Suddenly

there was a thundering rush, a wild flutter of wings. Daniel stopped. Grouse were flying everywhere, weaving crazily between the trees. One bird flew right at him. He threw his hands up in front of his face. Then the bird was gone.

Soon Daniel was down the mountain. Otter River was before him. He could see the snow-covered camp on the other side. He walked up and down the riverbank looking for a place to cross. Daniel knew that where the river ran still and deep the ice would be the thickest. There was a place like that about a hundred yards upstream. However, the river looked safe here, too. It wasn't quite so wide. Daniel took off his snowshoes. If he fell through with them on, his feet would be trapped under the ice. He stepped out onto the river and jumped up and down a couple of times. The ice was solid. He started across.

When he was almost to the far shore, he heard a loud, thundering crack begin near him and shoot up the river. Slowly, he began to sink. Then he heard more and louder cracks and a deep, rumbling roar. He was going down! The whole river was opening up!

Daniel threw his snowshoes onto the shore and grabbed for solid ice. His boots were full of water. His legs were numbed by the cold. Again and again he reached for the edge of solid ice. Each time the ice broke away and bobbed in front of him. Then his feet struck bottom. He stood waist deep in icy water. He could wade to shore. But there were great slabs of loose ice floating between him and the bank. When he tried to climb on top of them, they sank. When he tried to push them out of his way, they bumped into each other and blocked the way. He was trapped.

Daniel's mind raced. He had to think of something fast.

cold on his bare feet that it felt hot. When all his clothes were hung over the fire, he limped into the lean-to and climbed inside his sleeping bag. He shivered violently. He wanted to cry. However, he was too cold. Slowly, very slowly, his body heat began to fill the sleeping bag. He began to warm up. He took the bag of nuts and raisins from his pack and ate. He could see his clothes dripping and steaming over the fire. Daniel was relaxed now. His eyes grew heavy. He fell asleep.

When Daniel woke up, the fire was down to coals. It was warm inside the bag. He had no idea how long he had slept. It may have been an hour or two. He got up and put more wood on the fire. He felt his clothes. They were dry, except for his boots. He got dressed. His clothes smelled like wood smoke. He hung his boots from the pole by their laces and began to fix lunch. He set the bacon to frying in the skillet and put some snow to melt in the pail.

When the water boiled, he put the pail on a rock at the edge of the fire. He reached into his pack for the eggs. They were broken. They must have broken when he threw the pack up on the bank. He dumped them into his metal plate and separated shell from egg as best he could. He took the cooked bacon out of the skillet and put the eggs in, stirring them with his fork. They cooked quickly. Then he ate. It seemed to Daniel like the best meal he had ever eaten. Crisp bacon, scrambled eggs, good bread with butter, and cool water. It was good.

Daniel laughed to himself. Here he was, in the middle of winter, sitting by a fire, by a river he had just fallen into, eating lunch, thinking how good it was! It was hard to believe. A few hours ago he was almost dead. Now he

sat comfortably, his feet warmed by the fire, almost as if
nothing had happened.

When the last of his lunch was gone, he put his boots
on, cleaned and packed his gear, shoveled snow on the fire,
rolled the sleeping bag, and started home. This time he
headed to where the river moved slowly and the ice was
thick. Nobody ever crossed a frozen river more carefully
than Daniel did that afternoon.

When he reached the other side, he noticed that the sun
was low in the southern sky. It got dark early this time of
year. Home was a long way off. He'd have to travel quickly
to get there before dark.

He followed his own path up through the trees, over the
brow of the mountain, and down into the swamp.

By the time he reached the other side of the beaver pond, the sun was almost down. It was dark in the thick trees of the swamp. Daniel had trouble finding his path. It got darker and darker. He was hurrying now. Although it was growing colder, he was sweating. Then out of the darkening sky fear dropped down and seized him. He had gone off the path. He was lost.

He decided what to do. He would follow his tracks back to where he lost the path. He'd get back on the path and go home. It was hard to go back, but he had to do it.

When he found the path again, he moved along it slowly. It was so dark now he couldn't afford to get lost again. At last, after what seemed like hours, he found himself standing at the edge of a broad, open field. At the far end of the field he could see his house. The kitchen window glowed warm and orange in the dusky evening light. He struck off across the meadow toward the lighted window.

Answer these questions.

1. Why was the equipment Daniel was to carry on his hike so important to him?

2. How did Daniel learn about getting along in the woods? What was the most important thing that he was taught?

3. What happened to Daniel when he was crossing the river? How did he get back to the shore?

4. What did Daniel have to do after crossing the river? Why?

5. What happened to Daniel as he was going home? How did he solve his problem?

6. Why was it hard for Daniel to follow his tracks back to where he lost the path?

Write on your own.

Pretend that you are Daniel and that you are going to write in your diary about the day's adventures. Choose one of the events of the snowshoe hike and write a paragraph about it for the diary.

My Mom Is a Woodcarver

Becky Brown as told to Sallie Luther

Tools are very important. People use them every day in their work and at home. This article tells how one young person's mother uses tools in a very special way.

One day I came home to find a bear cub galloping across our kitchen floor! There was a bobcat on the counter! Another time there were two otters, a beaver, and a family of flying squirrels in our dining room.

Of course they were not alive. They sure *looked* real. You see, I'm very lucky. Mom's a woodcarver!

Mom's name is Avis Brown. We live in Adirondack Park in New York State. Grandpa was a lumberjack. Mom grew up right here in the woods. Nobody taught Mom how to carve. She just learned to do it herself. The more she practiced the better she got. Now she has her own business.

There are a lot of woodcarvers around. I think Mom is extra special. Other people must think so, too. Mom sells her statues as fast as she can carve them. She's even won contests!

Mom spends a lot of time watching animals when they aren't watching her. She tries to make sure that some of her carvings say something about how the forest animals live.

It's her animal faces I like best. Some of them grin or wink. Others look mad or sad. She'll carve a black-capped chickadee wearing a black cap or a frog that looks lonely. My all-time favorite is a fox looking very smart. All the while a mouse hides right under its feet. Of course everybody knows that birds don't wear hats. Frogs don't get sad, either. It's all part of the fun.

Something else that's fun is watching Mom carve. I can sit and watch her for hours! The animals just seem to come alive right on the workbench.

First Mom takes a piece of pine. She turns it around in

Copyright © 1981 National Wildlife Federation. Adapted from the August 1981 issue of *Ranger Rick* magazine, with permission of the publisher, the National Wildlife Federation.

her hands for a while. She says she's looking for a picture in the wood. She says the animal's already waiting in there. She just sets it free.

Anyway, Mom starts whittling away with her carving knife. The next thing you know, a foot or a tail or a nose is peeking out!

People often visit Mom's studio. They ask her two questions: What animals are your favorites? How do you do your carvings?

Mom tells them that the animal she's working on at the time is her favorite. (She really does love them all.) Then she shows them how she does her work.

What Mom does is called carving "in the round." That means creating a whole animal instead of a one-sided figure.

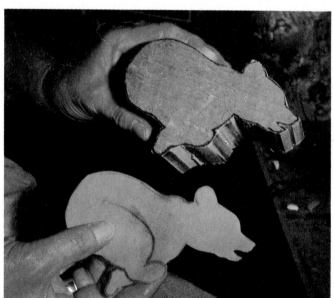
picture 1

First she draws an outline on a piece of white pine. Then she cuts out the rough shape (picture 1) with a big electric tool called a bandsaw.

picture 2

Next Mom shapes the carving (picture 2) with super-sharp knives and chisels. Then she uses a burning pen (picture 3) to burn that fur or feather look right into the wood.

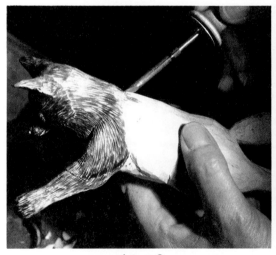

picture 3

picture 4

Painting each statue takes the longest time. That's where all the years of watching animals pays off. Mom makes sure every carving looks like the real thing.

Mom uses acrylic paints, which dry fast. Then she adds any finishing touches, like paintbrush bristles for whiskers (picture 4).

She mounts her statues on pieces of driftwood. We find the driftwood during "safaris" around the lakes here in the park. Boy, do we have some great times!

People always ask if I want to be a woodcarver too. I really don't know yet. Maybe so. Maybe I'll turn out to be a *real* chip off the old block!

Answer these questions.

1. What surprise did Becky receive one day when she returned home?

2. How did Avis Brown learn woodcarving?

3. Why does Avis turn the piece of wood around in her hands before she starts to carve?

4. What kind of carving does Avis do? Why is it called by this name?

5. How have the years that Avis has spent studying wildlife helped her with her woodcarving?

6. What kinds of things do you think Avis likes to do with her family? Why do you think so?

Reading in Science

Use your paper to complete the exercise below.

1. Look at the selection. What is the selection about?
2. Are there heads or subheads? What are they? What will each section be about?
3. Are any words in boldface or italic type? List them.
4. Skim the material and make a list of words that are unfamiliar to you. Write the meanings of these words by using clues in the sentence or a dictionary.
5. Read the selection. List the important details.
6. In your own words write a paragraph that summarizes the information in the selection. If possible, use the words that you listed as unfamiliar or use synonyms for these words.

The Ocean's Floor

What would the floor of the ocean look like if all of the water were drained away? It would look much like the dry land of the *continents.* There are *plains,* or flat areas, but there are also mountain ranges and valleys. If the highest land mountain, Mount Everest, were dropped into the deepest part of the ocean, its peak would be a mile underwater.

Mountains under the Sea

The ocean's mountains have no trees or snow and stand in darkness. The longest and widest mountain range is the Mid-Atlantic Ridge. It is more than three times longer than the Rocky Mountains. Most of the ridge lies underwater. Here and there, though, a peak rises above the surface. These form the islands of the Atlantic Ocean. The highest mountain on the earth is the volcano Mauna Kea of Hawaii in the Pacific Ocean. Only about a third of it rises above the water.

Valleys under the Sea

The valleys under the sea are much deeper than the valleys on land. Some of these are so deep that they have not yet been measured.

Think about sailing in a submarine across an ocean floor. What kind of plant life might you see? Books in the library will give you more information about the ocean, its floor, and its plant and animal life.

The Medicine Bag

Virginia Driving Hawk Sneve

People live in many different ways. What if your grandfather lives on a reservation? When Joe Iron Shell comes from a reservation for a visit, Martin must deal with some very mixed-up feelings. Can he live up to the pride that he has always felt for his Indian heritage and for his Indian great-grandfather? Or will he change?

My kid sister Cheryl and I always boasted about our Sioux grandpa, Joe Iron Shell. Our friends, who had always lived in the city and only knew about Indians from movies and TV, were impressed by our stories. Maybe we stretched the truth and made Grandpa sound glamorous, but when we'd return home to Iowa after our yearly

summer visit to Grandpa we always had some exciting tale to tell.

We always had some real Sioux gift to show our listeners. On one visit Grandpa gave me a small, round, flat, skin drum with a painting on it of a warrior riding a horse. He taught me a real Sioux chant to sing while I beat the drum with a leather-covered stick that had a feather on the end. That really got their attention.

We never showed our Grandpa's picture. Not that we weren't proud of him, but because we knew that the exciting tales we told didn't go with the real thing. Our friends would have laughed at the picture, because Grandpa wasn't tall and stately like TV Indians. His hair wasn't in braids, but hung in gray strings on his neck and he was old. He was our great-grandfather. He didn't live in a tipi, but all by himself in a part log, part tar-paper shed on the

Rosebud Reservation in South Dakota. So when Grandpa came to visit us, I was so worried I could've died.

There are a lot of fancy little dogs in our neighborhood, but they usually barked only at the mail carrier from the safety of their own yards. Now it sounded as if a whole pack were barking together in one place.

I got up and walked to the street to see what was causing all the noise. About a block away I saw a crowd of little kids yelling, with dogs barking and growling around someone who was walking down the middle of the street.

In the center of the strange parade was a man wearing a tall black hat. I felt cold and hot at the same time. "Oh no!" I whispered. "It's Grandpa!"

I stood on the curb. I couldn't move even though I wanted to run and hide. Then I got mad when I saw how the yippy dogs were snapping at the old man's baggy pant legs and how weakly he poked them away with his cane. "Stupid dogs," I said as I ran to help Grandpa.

"Grandpa," I said and felt pretty dumb when my voice cracked. I reached for his beat-up old tin case, which was tied shut with a rope. But he set it down right in the street and shook my hand.

"*Hau, Takoza*, Grandchild," he greeted me gravely in Sioux.

All I could do was stand there with the whole neighborhood watching and shake the hand of the leather-brown old man. I saw how his gray hair straggled from under his big black hat, which had a limp feather in its crown. His rumpled black suit hung like a sack over his stooped frame. As he shook my hand, his coat fell open, showing beneath it a bright-red satin shirt with a beaded bolo tie under the collar. His outfit wasn't out of place on the reservation, but it sure was here. I wanted to sink right through the street.

"Hi," I muttered with my head down. I tried to pull my hand away when I felt his bony hand trembling. When I looked up I could see from his face how tired he was. I felt like crying. I picked up Grandpa's case, took his arm, and guided him up the drive to our house.

Mom was standing on the steps.

"*Hau*, Marie," he said as he shook Mom's hand. She smiled and took his other arm.

As we helped him up the steps the door banged open and Cheryl came bursting out of the house. She was all smiles and was so openly glad to see Grandpa that I was ashamed of how I felt.

"Grandpa!" she yelled happily. "You came to see us."

Grandpa smiled and Mom and I let go of him as he stretched out his arms to my ten-year-old sister.

"*Wicincala*, little girl," he greeted her and then collapsed.

He had fainted. Mom and I carried him into the sewing room, where we had an extra bed.

After we had Grandpa on the bed, Mom stood there helplessly patting his shoulder.

"Shouldn't we call the doctor, Mom?" I asked.

"Yes," she agreed with a sigh. "You make Grandpa comfortable, Martin."

I knew Grandpa wouldn't want to have Mom undress him, but I didn't want to, either. He was so thin and frail that it was easy to slip his coat off. When I took off his tie and opened his shirt collar, I felt a small leather bag that hung from a cord around his neck. I left it alone and moved to remove his boots. The scuffed old cowboy boots were tight and he moaned as I jerked them off.

I put the boots on the floor and saw why they fit so tight. Each one was stuffed with money.

Mom came back with a bowl of water. "The doctor thinks Grandpa is suffering from heat exhaustion," she explained, as she bathed Grandpa's face. Mom gave a big sigh, "*Oh hinh*, Martin. How do you suppose he got here?"

We found out after the doctor's visit.

Between sips of soup Grandpa told us of his journey. Soon after our visit to him Grandpa decided that he would like to see where his only living family lived and what our

home was like. Besides, he added sheepishly, he was lonesome after we left.

I knew everybody felt as bad as I did—especially Mom. Mom was all Grandpa had left. So even after she married my dad, and after Cheryl and I were born, Mom made sure that every summer we spent a week with Grandpa.

I never thought that Grandpa would be lonely after our visits, and none of us noticed how old and weak he had become. Grandpa knew, though, and so he came to us. He had traveled on buses for two and a half days. When he arrived in the city, tired and stiff from sitting for so long, he set out, walking, to find us.

He had stopped to rest on the steps of some building downtown and a police officer found him. The officer, Grandpa said, was a good person who took him to the bus stop and told the driver to let Grandpa out at Bell View Drive. After Grandpa got off the bus, he started walking again. But he couldn't see the house numbers on the other side when he walked on the sidewalk, so he walked in the middle of the street. That's when all the little kids and dogs followed him.

I knew everybody felt as bad as I did. Yet I was proud of this eighty-six-year-old man, who had never been away

from the reservation, having the courage to travel so far alone.

"You found the money in my boots?" he asked Mom.

"Martin did," she answered.

"The money is what I've saved for a long time—a hundred dollars—for my funeral. I want you to take it now to buy groceries so that I won't be a trouble to you while I am here."

"No, Grandpa," Dad said. "We are honored to have you with us and you will never be trouble to us. I am only sorry that we never thought to bring you home with us this summer and spare you this long trip."

Grandpa was pleased. "Thank you," he answered. "Do not feel bad that you didn't bring me with you, for I would not have come then. It was not time." He said this in such a way that no one could argue with him. To Grandpa and the Sioux, he once told me, a thing would be done when it was the right time to do it, and that's the way it was.

"Also," Grandpa went on, looking at me, "I have come because it is soon time for Martin to have the medicine bag."

We all knew what that meant. Grandpa thought he was going to die and he had to follow the tradition of his family to pass the medicine bag, along with its history, to the oldest male child.

I didn't know what to say. I had the same hot and cold feeling that I had when I first saw Grandpa in the street. The medicine bag was the dirty leather pouch I had found around his neck. "I could never wear such a thing," I almost said aloud. I thought of having my friends see it at the swimming pool, and could imagine the smart things they would say. I just swallowed hard and took a step toward the bed. I knew I would have to take it.

Grandpa was tired. "Not now, Martin," he said, waving his hand to dismiss us, "it is not time. Now I will sleep."

So that's how Grandpa came to be with us for two months. My friends kept asking to come see the old man, but I put them off. I told myself that I didn't want them laughing at Grandpa. Even as I made excuses I knew it wasn't Grandpa that I was afraid they'd laugh at.

Nothing bothered Cheryl about bringing her friends to see Grandpa. Every day after school started there'd be a bunch of little girls or boys crowded around the old man.

Grandpa would smile in his gentle way and answer their questions, or he'd tell them stories. The kids listened in awed silence. Those little guys thought Grandpa was great.

Finally, one day after school my friends came home with me because nothing I said stopped them.

When we got to my house Grandpa was sitting on the patio. He had on his red shirt, but today he also wore a fringed leather vest sewn on top with beads. Instead of his cowboy boots he wore beaded moccasins. Of course, he had his old black hat on—he was almost never without it. It had been brushed and the feather in the beaded headband was standing up proudly, its tip a brighter white. His hair was in silver strands over the red shirt collar.

I stared just as my friends did, and I heard one of them murmur, "Wow!"

Grandpa looked up and when his eyes met mine, they twinkled as if he were laughing inside. He nodded to me and my face got all hot. I could tell that he had known all along I was afraid he'd embarrass me in front of my friends.

"*Hau, hoksilas,* boys," he greeted and held out his hand.

My friends passed in a single file and shook his hand as I introduced them. They were so polite I almost laughed.

"You look fine, Grandpa," I said as the guys sat on the lawn chairs or on the floor.

"*Hanh,* yes," he agreed. "When I woke up this morning it seemed the right time to dress in the good clothes. I knew that my grandson would be bringing his friends."

"You guys want something to drink?" I offered. No one answered. They were listening to Grandpa as he started telling how he'd killed the deer from which his vest was made.

Grandpa did most of the talking while my friends were there. I was so proud of him and amazed at how respectfully quiet my friends were. Mom had to chase them home at supper time. As they left they shook Grandpa's hand again and said to me:

"Martin, he's really great!"

"Yeah, man! Don't blame you for keeping him to yourself."

"Can we come back?"

After they left, Mom said, "No more visitors for a while, Martin. Grandpa won't admit it, but he is still not very strong."

All night I had strange dreams about thunder and lightning on a high hill. From a distance I heard the slow beat of a drum. At school it seemed as if the day would never end and, when it finally did, I ran home.

Grandpa was in his room, sitting on the bed. The shades were down and the place was dim and cool. I sat on the floor in front of Grandpa, but he didn't even look at me. After what seemed a long time he spoke.

"I sent your mother and sister away. What you will

hear today is only for your ears. What you will receive is only for your hands.'' He fell silent and I felt shivers down my back.

"My father in his youth," Grandpa began, "made a vision quest to find a spirit guide for his life. You cannot understand how it was in that time, when the great Teton Sioux were first made to stay on the reservation. There was a strong need for guidance from *Wakantanka*, the Great Spirit. Too many of the young men were filled with despair and hate. They thought it was hopeless to search for a vision. My father, however, held to the old ways.

"He carefully prepared for his search with a purifying sweat bath and then he went alone to a high butte top to fast and pray. After three days he received his sacred dream—in which he found, after long searching, the white man's iron. He did not understand his dream of finding something belonging to the white people, for in that time they were the enemy. When he came down from the butte to cleanse himself at the stream below, he found the remains of a campfire and the broken shell of an iron kettle. This sign seemed to bear out his dream. He took a piece of the iron for his medicine bag.

"He returned to his village, where he told his dream to the wise old men of the tribe. They gave him the name *Iron Shell,* but neither did they understand the meaning of the dream. This first Iron Shell kept the piece of iron with him at all times, and believed that it protected him in those unhappy days.

"Then a terrible thing happened to Iron Shell. He and several other young men were taken from their homes by the soldiers and sent far away to a white man's boarding school. At first Iron Shell fought against the teachers' attempts to change him, and he did not try to learn. One day it was his turn to work in the school's blacksmith shop. As he walked into the place, he knew that his medicine had brought him there to learn and work with the white man's iron.

"Iron Shell became a blacksmith and worked at the trade when he returned to the reservation. All of his life he treasured the medicine bag. When he was old, and I was a man, he gave it to me, for no one made the vision quest anymore."

Grandpa quit talking and I stared in shock as he covered his face with his hands. His shoulders were shaking with quiet sobs and I looked away until he began to speak again.

"I kept the bag until my son, your mother's father, was a man and had to leave us to fight in the war across the ocean. I gave him the bag, for I believed it would protect him in battle, but he did not take it with him. He was afraid that he would lose it. He died in a far-off place."

Again Grandpa was still and I felt his sorrow around me.

He unbuttoned his shirt, pulled out the leather pouch, and lifted it over his head. He held it in his hand, turning it over and over as if memorizing how it looked.

"In the bag," he said as he opened it and removed two objects, "is the broken shell of the iron kettle, a pebble from the butte, and a piece of the sacred sage." He held the pouch upside down and dust drifted down.

"After the bag is yours, you must put a piece of sage inside it and never open it again until you pass it on to your son." He put the pebble and the piece of iron back into the bag, and tied it.

I stood up, somehow knowing I should. Grandpa slowly rose from the bed and stood up straight in front of me, holding the bag before my face. I closed my eyes and waited for him to slip it over my head. Instead he spoke.

"No, you need not wear it." He placed the soft leather bag in my right hand and closed my other hand over it. "It would not be right to wear it in this time and place where no one will understand. Put it safely away until you are again on the reservation. Wear it then, when you find the sacred sage."

Grandpa turned and sat again on the bed. Weakly he leaned his head against the pillow. "Go," he said, "I will sleep now."

"Thank you, Grandpa," I said softly and left with the bag in my hands.

That night Mom and Dad took Grandpa to the hospital. Two weeks later I stood alone on the lonely prairie of the reservation and put the sacred sage in my bag.

Answer these questions.

1. Why was Martin ashamed of his Sioux great-grandfather at the beginning of the story? Why was Martin proud of him?

2. Why wouldn't Grandpa have come home with Martin and his family during the summer? Why did Grandpa choose to come when he did?

3. Why didn't Martin want his friends to meet his great-grandfather? How did Martin's friends act when they did meet him?

4. What vision or dream did Grandpa's father have? How did it come true?

5. What was in the medicine bag?

6. What did Martin do that showed he was proud to have the medicine bag?

Animal Tools

George F. Mason

Fur and feathers, teeth and claws—animals seem remarkably fitted for their lives. However, they need more than weapons. Read this article to find out the amazing ways that animals meet their needs.

When was the last time you used tools? People often use tools. Sometimes they use their hands as tools. Most of the time, though, they hold the tools with their hands and do the work with the tools.

Most animals use parts of their bodies as tools. Probably the most important tools animals have are their teeth.

Animal teeth are used for cutting and grinding food, but they may be used for other reasons, too. Animals such as foxes have long, sharp eye-teeth, which they use in killing or fighting. Beavers have long front teeth, which they can use to cut down trees. Rabbits and many other animals also have long front teeth. They are used to bite off bark and twigs.

The animals that eat grass have another kind of teeth. Their teeth are wide and flat and are used for grinding food. Cows and deer have teeth of this kind.

The largest teeth that we know of are the tusks of the elephants. The elephants use their tusks in digging for food and in fighting.

One unusual set of animal tools is that used by a mosquito for getting food. A mosquito doesn't really bite, as many people think it does. It can't bite, for it has no teeth.

If you watch a mosquito, you will see that it seems to push its bill into the skin, but this isn't what really happens. The mosquito's bill is only its lower lip. But inside the lip is a set of tiny tools. There are a pair of saws, a pair of tubes, and some tiny knives in this set of tools. The mosquito uses all of them when it gets food.

When a mosquito is hungry, it looks for a soft spot in an animal's skin. After finding this spot, it puts its bill on the skin and begins to cut. The tiny saws and knives in the set of tools quickly cut through the skin. Then the two tubes in the bill are pushed in. One puts saliva into the blood to keep it thin. The other sucks up blood.

Only the female mosquito has this strange set of tools, for the male does not live on blood. It lives on plant juices instead.

Another strange set of tools is the bittern's cleaning tools. This bird has powder puffs, fine powder, combs, and feather oil. On each leg the bittern has some soft, fluffy feathers that hold the fine powder. Under the middle toe on each foot there is a comb. And on the top part of the tail there is a place where the feather oil comes out.

The bittern often feeds on fish or eels. When it catches and eats these animals, it gets slime on its feathers. The bird spends one to two hours cleaning up after each feeding.

First it puts the fine powder on its feathers. The powder makes the feathers look as though they had been dusted with flour. The bird lets this dry on its feathers. Then it uses its combs to loosen the dried slime. After much shaking of the feathers, all the powder and the loose slime are gone. Next the bittern gets oil with its bill from its tail. The bird puts this oil over its feathers. Soon the bird is clean, and the feathers are shiny again.

Bitterns aren't the only animals that have combs. Beavers and a few other animals have combs, too. Beavers have a comb that is part of the nail on the second toe of each back foot. Since they are very clean animals, they spend a lot of time combing their thick fur and keeping it clean and soft.

Besides the tools you've just read about, there are many others. Can you think of any other tools that you have seen animals using?

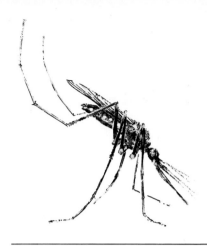

Answer these questions.

1. How do animal tools usually differ from tools that people use?

2. For what kinds of things can animals use their teeth?

3. What kinds of tools does a female mosquito use to get her food? How does a female mosquito use the tools?

4. What does a male mosquito live on?

5. What kinds of tools does a bittern use to clean itself?

6. Why don't all animals have combs like the bittern and the beaver or saws like the mosquito?

Reading Product Directions

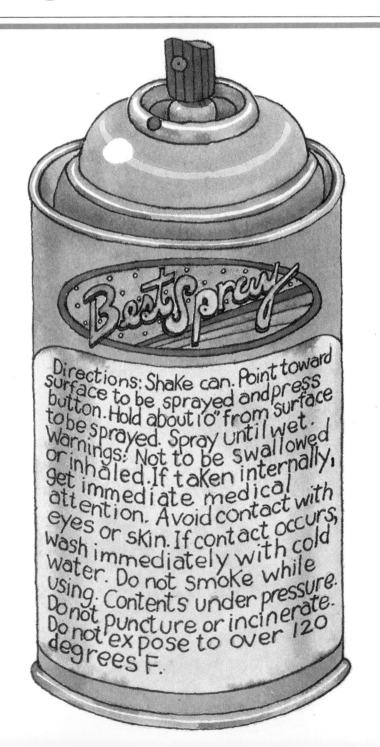

Best Spray

Directions: Shake can. Point toward surface to be sprayed and press button. Hold about 10" from surface to be sprayed. Spray until wet. Warnings: Not to be swallowed or inhaled. If taken internally, get immediate medical attention. Avoid contact with eyes or skin. If contact occurs, wash immediately with cold water. Do not smoke while using. Contents under pressure. Do not puncture or incinerate. Do not expose to over 120 degrees F.

A. On your paper answer the following questions.

1. How far should the can be away from the surface to be sprayed?
   a. very far
   b. about 10′
   c. very close
   d. about 10″
2. What words tell you that this is for use outside the body only?
   a. Not to be swallowed or inhaled.
   b. If taken internally, get immediate medical attention.
   c. Both a and b
3. What does "Do not puncture or incinerate" tell you?
   a. not to put a hole in or set fire to
   b. to throw the can away
   c. to keep the can in a cold place
   d. not to use the spray in large rooms

B. These words are often seen on labels. Match the words with their definitions. Write the answers on your paper.

   1. avoid   a. what is inside
   2. contents   b. stay away from
   3. expose   c. to burn
   4. incinerate   d. to place near
   5. inhale   e. to happen
   6. internal   f. to pierce
   7. occur   g. to breathe in
   8. puncture   h. within the body

Poetry

Some poems are about brave things that people have done. Others are about wonderfully beautiful places. However, some poems are about everyday things. In these poems three poets tell the special feelings they have for things that some people may see every day.

Skyscrapers

Do skyscrapers ever grow tired
Of holding themselves up high?
Do they ever shiver on frosty nights
With their tops against the sky?
Do they feel lonely sometimes
Because they have grown so tall?
Do they ever wish they could lie right down
And never get up at all?

Rachel Field

354

The Deserted House

There's no smoke in the chimney,
    And the rain beats on the floor;
There's no glass in the window,
    There's no wood in the door;
The heather grows behind the house,
    And the sand lies before.

No hand hath trained the ivy,
    The walls are gray and bare;
The boats upon the sea sail by,
    Nor ever tarry there.
No beast of the field comes nigh,
    Nor any bird of the air.

Mary Coleridge

The Eagle

He clasps the crag with crooked hands;
Close to the sun in lonely lands,
Ring'd with the azure world, he stands,

The wrinkled sea beneath him crawls;
He watches from his mountain walls,
And like a thunderbolt he falls.

Alfred, Lord Tennyson

Answer these questions.

1. What does Rachel Field ask about skyscrapers that makes these buildings seem to be like people?

2. What do the chimney, the window, the door, and the field not have that shows that the house is a deserted one?

3. How is an eagle like a thunderbolt?

4. How do the poets seem to feel about skyscrapers, the deserted house, and the eagle?

Write on your own.

Write a poem that compares a peacock to a fan or a shark to a submarine. In the poem list ways in which the animal and the object are alike.

Grand Papa and Ellen Aroon

F. N. Monjo

Grand Papa is not only Ellen Aroon's grandfather. He is also the president of a new country, the United States. As president, Grand Papa has many friends and also some enemies. One group of enemies, "the Feds," call Grand Papa "Mr. Mammoth." That is because he collects old bones of dinosaurs and other prehistoric animals. Ellen and her Grand Papa, Thomas Jefferson, have some very special feelings for each other. In this story, Ellen tells about the United States, Thomas Jefferson, and herself.

In Washington City

Washington City is just a tiny town. Grand Papa says there aren't but 3,210 people living there. The streets are muddy. Grand Papa had some poplar trees planted along Pennsylvania Avenue, but they're still just tiny.

Only part of the Capitol is finished. And the President's House isn't finished either. Some of the rooms don't have any plaster on the ceilings. Mama says it's a big drafty barn.

Grand Papa says it's big enough for "two emperors, one pope, and the grand lama in the bargain." There aren't any stone steps up to the front door yet. You have to walk up a wooden ramp to get to the entrance hall.

Grand Papa and Papa were mighty glad to see Mama and all of us children. Grand Papa has a steward here who's French, named Etienne Lemaire. He lets us have pancakes for breakfast. Guess how he spells pancakes. *Pannequaques!* (That's because he's French!)

Sometimes Grand Papa has to have big dinners at night for the ambassadors from England and France and Spain.

Jeff says one night, when Grand Papa had a big dinner, the Dutch ambassador was there. Everybody helped themselves to a spoonful of sticky white pudding. Then the Dutch ambassador dropped his napkin. When he leaned down to pick it up, by accident his chin whiskers went into the pudding on his plate! Jeff heard the poor man whisper, "I vish I vass dead!" (I reckon he was embarrassed!)

You know who Grand Papa hates? Napoleon. He's the emperor of the French. Grand Papa says Napoleon wants to rule the whole world. Grand Papa calls Napoleon "a most determined villain."

Mama says Napoleon used to own a great big chunk of land, called Louisiana, right next to our country. But three years ago, Mama says, Grand Papa started trying to buy the whole parcel. So he sent a friend of his—Mr. James Monroe—over to France to talk to Napoleon.

When Mr. Monroe bought it for him, Grand Papa *doubled* the size of our country! He didn't need any extra taxes to do it. He didn't go to war for it, either!

Mama made me figure it out in an arithmetic lesson. Here's how much Grand Papa had to pay for Louisiana: $15,000,000. Here's what he got for the money: 1,171,931 square miles of land. Mama says Louisiana cost Grand Papa about $12.80 per square mile. She says that's quite a good bargain! Of course Grand Papa is still just *guessing* at how much land is out there. Nobody knows for sure. Nobody knows how far it stretches, or just who lives there.

Grand Papa says there may be wooly mammoths or even dinosaurs still living out there! He says somewhere in it, it may have a huge mountain of salt!

The Feds laugh at Grand Papa. They say, "Isn't that just like Mr. Mammoth? Next thing he'll be telling us there's a valley full of corn pudding way up the Missouri River, and a great big lake of molasses!"

Grand Papa doesn't care how much the Feds laugh at him. He's sent Meriwether Lewis (who used to be his private secretary) and William Clark, and some soldiers and trappers out there to see what they can see. He wants them

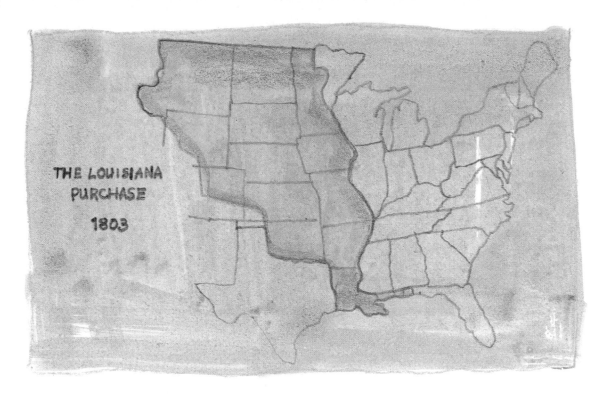

THE LOUISIANA PURCHASE 1803

to go all the way up the Missouri River, and clear on out to the Pacific Ocean, if they can!

I've gotten to know Mrs. Dolley Madison. Dolley Madison is married to short, little old James Madison. Mr. Madison is one of Grand Papa's best friends. He's Grand Papa's secretary of state, and helps him run things in Washington City.

Dolley Madison told me how it was when Grand Papa first came in, as President, way back on March 4, 1801. She told me about the parade they had, in Philadelphia, for Grand Papa. There were only sixteen states then. Now there are seventeen. In the parade there were sixteen white horses hitched to a carriage. One horse for every state of the Union. Set on top of the carriage was a big ship of state with sails set and flags flying. It was called the *Thomas Jefferson*. People shot off cannons and cheered.

Dolley Madison told me how all kinds of Indian chiefs come here to talk to Grand Papa when he has his Galas on the Fourth of July and on New Year's Day. A Gala is a big party. Grand Papa won't have any parties any other time but New Year's Day and the Fourth of July.

Grand Papa told me that one year some farmers from Massachusetts made him a present of a great big enormous cheese. It was four feet wide, and it weighed 1,235 pounds. That's more than half a ton! But Grand Papa wouldn't take it as a gift. He paid the men $200 for it. Grand Papa doesn't believe in taking presents while he's president.

Yesterday Grand Papa let me eat a new dessert made by his French cook. Nobody in this country has ever tasted it before. It's called ice cream.

Now I have to tell you about Dick. Dick is Grand Papa's pet mockingbird. Grand Papa keeps him in a cage in his study. Lots of times he lets Dick out of his cage. Dick sits on Grand Papa's shoulder. He flies around from chair to chair. Grand Papa loves mockingbirds. I don't know what he'd do without Dick. Grand Papa once told Sister Anne

and Jeff and Cornelia and Virginia and Mary and me that if we *ever* harmed a mockingbird, or stole eggs from its nest, the mockingbirds would come back and haunt us! Mama says it's true!

At Monticello

We're all back home at Edgehill. Even Papa is here. Papa's full name is Thomas Mann Randolph. He's part Indian. He has dark hair. He's descended from Pocahontas.

Later on this summer Grand Papa will come to Virginia, too. Here's the first thing Grand Papa does when he comes to Edgehill. He carries every single one of us over to *his* house, Monticello, to be with him all summer long: Mama and Papa, Sister Anne and Jeff, Cornelia, Virginia, Mary, baby James Madison, and me, Ellen Aroon! Grand Papa wants all of us with him, Uncle Jack Eppes and Francis and Maria, and all of our aunts and uncles and cousins. He wants his whole family to be with him at Monticello.

You can see Monticello from Edgehill. It's way up on top of a mountain, about four or five miles away. Grand Papa says its name means "Little Mountain" in Italian. Grand Papa named it, and found the mountain he wanted to build it on, and drew the plans for the house all by himself.

Mama says Grand Papa is a fine architect. There's no other house quite like it in Virginia, or in the whole world. From way up there, you can look in every direction for miles and miles. Most people want their houses to look bigger than they really are, but Grand Papa designed Monticello to look *smaller* than it really is. Monticello really has three stories, but Grand Papa designed it to look as if it

hadn't got but one! Isn't that *just* like Grand Papa? He thinks Monticello is the loveliest spot on earth. So does Mama. So do I.

Grand Papa orders plants and shrubs and trees from all over the world for his hilltop. They come from France and Italy and China and Spain. He has every kind of tree you can think of: flowering trees, shade trees, evergreen trees, nut trees, fruit trees. He grows walnuts and pecans, chestnuts, hickory nuts, and butternuts, apples, pears, and strawberries, grapes and plums, raspberries and currants, persimmons and figs, and peaches, watermelons, and nectarines. His gardeners, Wormley and Goliath, grow celery and radishes, asparagus and lettuce, cauliflower and onions, carrots and beets, corn and squash, broccoli, spinach, and beans. And they grow Grand Papa's favorite vegetable, green peas.

I quit counting how many different kinds of peas there

were, after I counted nineteen! Peas are one of the first vegetables to get ripe for the table in spring. Do you know what Grand Papa does when his very first mess of garden peas are ready to eat in the springtime? He asks all his neighbors to come to dinner, to help him celebrate.

One time, when the peas came in, Grand Papa asked Mr. and Mrs. Madison to come to dinner. Mr. Madison likes to lean back in his chair at the table, and he was sitting in front of an open window that goes right down to the floor. Mr. Madison likes to imitate politicians. He was imitating Patrick Henry.

"Here's what Patrick Henry says about Mr. Jefferson," said Mr. Madison. "He says Mr. Jefferson eats so much fine French cooking, he's quit eating all his favorite Virginia foods. No more ham! No more cornbread! He has abjured his native vittles!" And Mr. Madison commenced laughing so hard, he fell backwards, right out of the window onto the lawn!

The next day, Grand Papa told Heming, the carpenter, to put railings on all those windows.

Then there's Uncle Isaac. He works at Monticello. Uncle Isaac remembers the Revolution. He told me about the time—when he was just a little boy about seven—when the British cavalry rode up the mountain to Monticello, trying to capture Grand Papa. Grand Papa knew they were coming, so he was able to ride away in plenty of time. But Isaac stayed behind, here, to help bury the silverware under the porch. The British never got hold of it.

Do you know why the British wanted to catch Grand Papa? They were angry with him. It was because of a letter he wrote to their king, King George III. Mama says *he* was a tyrant, too! What Grand Papa wrote was not a letter, really. It was more like an *announcement*. What Grand Papa wrote in it was that from now on everybody in America was going to be free. It was called the Declaration of Independence. Grand Papa showed me the little writing desk he wrote it on. He had the desk made in Philadelphia. It's in his library.

Mama says Grand Papa finished writing the Declaration of Independence on July 4, 1776. Mama says that's why we have barbecue and fireworks every year on this day. If it wasn't for Grand Papa, we wouldn't have any reason at all to celebrate the Fourth of July!

Mama got a letter from Grand Papa today. Guess what happened. He's heard from Lewis and Clark—the men he sent out to explore Louisiana. They're safe! They'll be coming home! They traveled thousands and thousands of miles. They got to the headwaters of the Missouri River. They found the place where it splits up into three rivers.

Mama says Meriwether Lewis and William Clark got to the Pacific Ocean. An Indian girl, named Sacajawea, helped them to find horses so they could cross the mountains. They're going to send some Indians to Washington City to meet Grand Papa.

Do you know what happened after that? Grand Papa came home from Washington City to Virginia for his summer vacation. First he rode to Edgehill on his favorite horse, Castor. He came real early in the morning and he crept upstairs and he *caught me in bed!* I was fast asleep!

"Ellen Aroon!" said Grand Papa. "You're a sleepyhead. And I've caught you in bed again!"

Sister Anne told Grand Papa she *knew* he'd catch me in

bed. She says I'm lazy, and I take too long dressing. Mama and Grand Papa just laughed, and we all went downstairs for a breakfast of biscuits and jam.

Mama asked Grand Papa if he'd remembered to bring her the coffee cups. "I'll need them for the summer visitations," said Mama. She means all the visitors who come to see Grand Papa at Monticello in summer.

Sometimes Mama has to feed *fifty* people for dinner. Grand Papa never runs strangers away, not if they have letters from friends of his. Sometimes the visitors stay for weeks and weeks. Grand Papa doesn't seem to mind.

Here's how Grand Papa spends his day resting at Monticello. He gets up at daybreak. If it's chilly his servant, Burwell, makes him a fire in the fireplace. Then Grand Papa reads, or writes letters before breakfast. Grand Papa has a machine in his study that makes a second copy of his letters while he writes them! It's called a polygraph.

Grand Papa has a leather chair that swivels around and around. He invented it himself. He lets me turn around and around on it whenever I want.

"Grand Papa," I said, "it spins around just like a top or a whirligig." (A whirligig is a toy, and you blow in at one end of a hollow tube, and then a little paddle wheel at the other end spins around in a jet of air.)

"It *does* spin around like a whirligig, Ellen Aroon," said Grand Papa. "And that's just what the Feds have called it, Mr. Jefferson's *whirligig chair!*" We have a good laugh at the Feds.

Sometimes Grand Papa reads in his study before breakfast. When Grand Papa is looking something up in his books, he sometimes takes down fifteen or twenty books at a time. Then he spreads them out on the floor and paces back and forth, from book to book. Here's how many books Grand Papa has in his library: 9,000. Here's all the different languages that Grand Papa can read: Latin, Greek, Anglo-Saxon, French, Spanish, Italian, and English!

Then Grand Papa goes to breakfast in the dining room. And then, around nine, he goes to the stables. I reckon Grand Papa loves horses more than any other animal in the world. He goes for long, long rides down by the river to see his mill, and he rides over his fields. Grand Papa looks over his crops for hours and hours, and doesn't come home until dinnertime, at three in the afternoon.

When there's company at dinner, sometimes we don't get up from the table until five o'clock. Before the sun goes down, we children go walking with Grand Papa.

Sometimes, at sunset, we sit on the portico, watching the sun go down over the Blue Ridge Mountains. When Grand Papa looks up at the ceiling, the inside weather vane there tells him which way the wind is blowing outdoors.

Tonight, when it gets dark enough, Grand Papa is going

to take us up to the top of the house, into the dome, and let us look through his telescope. He's going to show us the rings of Saturn. Saturn is a planet, and it has these pretty bands, or rings, around it.

Right now, we're waiting for it to get good and dark. All of us children are playing a game with Grand Papa.

Finally, it's dark enough for all of us to go up into the dome and look at the rings of Saturn. We all stand there quietly while Grand Papa focuses the lens of his telescope. Then at last he says, "There she is!" and lets me be the first to look. They look so pretty I just forget everything Mama ever told me, and I say: "They're mighty pretty, Mr. Mammoth!"

Grand Papa looks at me, real deep into my eyes, and we both begin to laugh. Grand Papa is still laughing when he takes me up to bed and kisses me good night. "Yes, mighty pretty," says Grand Papa. "Mighty pretty, Ellen Aroon!"

Answer these questions.

1. Why did Thomas Jefferson send Meriwether Lewis and William Clark to Louisiana?

2. What did Thomas Jefferson write and send to King George III of England?

3. How did Ellen Aroon feel about Monticello?

4. What did Thomas Jefferson invent? What languages did he speak?

5. What did Grand Papa, Ellen Aroon, and Ellen's family see when they looked through the telescope?

6. What kind of person was Thomas Jefferson?

The Case of the Treasure Map

Donald J. Sobol

Encyclopedia Brown was known as Encyclopedia because he knew so much about so many things. He used what he knew to run his business, the Brown Detective Agency. Encyclopedia's father was the chief of police for the town of Idaville. Encyclopedia was so successful with his business that sometimes his father asked him for his help. In this chapter from the book Encyclopedia Brown Saves the Day, *Encyclopedia solves a mystery involving buried treasure. All the clues are given in the story. See if you can find the clues and come up with the answer.*

Winslow Brant was Idaville's master snooper. No ash can was safe from him.

Snooping had rewarded him well. Already he owned the finest collection of bottle caps in the neighborhood.

He wasn't snooping, however, when he came into the Brown Detective Agency. He was drooping.

"I nearly had it all," he moaned. He sagged against the wall.

"Had what?" asked Encyclopedia.

"Treasure," said Winslow. "The dream of every great snooper—treasure!"

"Your big chance slipped through your fingers?"

"No, it *ran*," said Winslow. He whipped out a piece of cloth. The colors had run together. "It was a map showing where Henri La Farge buried some of his treasure!"

Everyone in the state knew of the pirate Henri La Farge. Two hundred years ago he had made his hideout among the small islands south of Idaville. There, someplace, he buried a fortune.

"The map was in a broken music box. I found it yesterday morning on the Smiths' trash pile," said Winslow. Then he told his sad story.

He had showed the map to Pete Alders. Pete was sixteen and owned a sailboat. He had agreed to take Winslow to the islands for a share of the treasure.

The boys had reached their destination after dark. They spent the night aboard ship. In the morning, Winslow had found the map drying on deck. Pete said he had used it to plug a leak during the night. In the dark, he had thought he was using a pillowcase.

"I'll bet Pete first made a copy of the map so he can have

all the treasure," said Winslow. "After he brought me home, he returned to the islands."

"He won't find anything there," said Encyclopedia. He pointed to a tiny black smudge on the map.

"I never noticed that," said Winslow. "What is it?"

"It *was* writing," replied Encyclopedia. "It said, 'New York World's Fair.' Your map was just a souvenir that cost fifty cents. My dad had one for years."

"Well, I'll be cow-kicked," said Winslow. Suddenly his face lit up. "Pete's off digging for treasure. *He thinks!* Serves him right!"

"We don't know that Pete ruined your map on purpose," Encyclopedia said.

"I'll hire you," said Winslow. "If you find out that Pete copied my map, don't tell him the truth. Let him dig."

Encyclopedia agreed. Two hours later the boys were heading toward the islands.

They looked at five islands. Then they spied Pete's sailboat. She was in a small cove. One of her portholes was open.

"Pete will be digging by a group of three coconut trees," said Winslow, hopping ashore. "The map showed a treasure chest was buried at the foot of the center tree."

After a short walk, the boys spied three coconut trees growing close together. Pete was there. He was digging in the hot sun.

"Boy, he looks ready to lean on his tongue," said Winslow happily.

"He believes those trees are the ones on the map," replied Encyclopedia.

Pete was surprised to see the boys. He gave Winslow a

weak smile. He climbed out of the hole. "You know I'll split what I find with you," he said.

"Sure, Pete," said Winslow. "And I see you fixed the sailboat. I never did ask you where the leak was."

"Well . . . ah . . . it was . . . ah . . . a porthole," said Pete. "It wouldn't close."

"One was stuck," said Winslow. "I remember."

The older boy said, "You lay down in the cabin last night. I stayed on deck checking things. I saw that we had anchored at low tide. In a little while, the tide started coming in."

"You see very well in the dark," said Encyclopedia.

"There was moonlight," said Pete. "I could see the high water mark on the shore. It was then about two and a half feet above the water level."

"What has high and low tide got to do with my map getting wet?" demanded Winslow.

"The tide rose about five inches an hour," said Pete. "The portholes are eighteen inches above the water. In less than four hours the tide would rise to the open porthole. Water would pour in and sink the boat."

"So you plugged the porthole and saved the boat," said Winslow. "With my map!"

"That was a mistake. I told you," said Pete. "The cabin was dark. I thought I had a pillowcase. Honest."

Winslow looked uncertain. He turned to Encyclopedia. He whispered, "Pete may be telling the truth."

"No, he wet your map to keep you from finding buried treasure," said Encyclopedia. "His story doesn't hold water!"

WHY NOT?

Solution to "The Case of the Treasure Map"

Encyclopedia knew that Pete had ruined Winslow's map after first making a copy to use.

The boy detective saw through Pete's story about the porthole.

Pete claimed that the tide was rising "about five inches an hour." That part was true.

Pete also said that he was afraid the water would rise above the open porthole. It was "eighteen inches above the water" when he had dropped anchor.

However, the rising tide would never have reached the open porthole even if it rose twice as fast.

The boat would have risen too!

Winslow let Pete dig up the island for another hour. Then he told Pete that the "treasure" map was nothing but a souvenir of the World's Fair.

About the Author

Donald J. Sobol has written many books for children and adults. He has also written over one hundred stories that have been published in magazines. He writes stories that center on the plot, the happenings in the story, rather than on characters. He has written several Encyclopedia Brown books for children. Each book is filled with action.

Answer these questions.

1. Does Winslow know the value of the things that he finds? How do you know?

2. Why had Winslow agreed to share the treasure with Pete?

3. What did Encyclopedia see on the map that showed that the map was a fake?

4. How did Encyclopedia know what the smeared printing had said?

5. Had the Smiths probably known that the map was a fake? How do you know?

6. How did Encyclopedia know that Pete wasn't telling the truth about saving the boat by using Winslow's map?

Reading in Health

Use your paper to complete the exercise below.

1. Look at the selection. What is the selection about?
2. Are there heads or subheads? What are they? What will each section be about?
3. Are any words in boldface or italic type? List them.
4. Skim the material and make a list of words that are unfamiliar to you. Write the meanings of these words by using clues in the sentence or a dictionary.
5. Read the selection. List the important details.
6. In your own words write a paragraph that summarizes the information in the selection. If possible, use the words that you listed as unfamiliar or use synonyms for these words.

Taking Care of Your Eyes

By remembering a few simple things, people can prevent serious eye problems.

Check-ups

The most important thing anyone can do in caring for the eyes is to visit the doctor regularly. People should have *annual,* or yearly, check-ups. Any problems that the eye doctor may find during these visits can then be cared for in early stages.

Safety Measures

Many things may be done to help prevent accidents that may damage the eyes or even cause blindness.

People who wear eyeglasses should have lenses made of unbreakable glass or plastic.

People who work in places where metal or wood chips are thrown or where sparks fly should wear safety goggles.

People who work in places where they are around strong lights such as sun lamps or welding gear should wear darkened glasses.

First Aid

Use water to rinse away objects caught in the eye. The corner of a clean cloth also may be used. If this does not work, see a doctor. Never rub the eye. This may cause scratches, which are serious and painful.

Vocabulary Review

On your paper write **a, b, c,** or **d** to show the item that best completes the sentence.

1. We sailed our ship into the island's cove, or _____.
   a. tunnel   c. boy
   b. bay   d. porthole

2. To enter a chamber is to enter a _____.
   a. rule   c. vehicle
   b. talk   d. room

3. To say frozen things thaw means that they _____.
   a. malt   c. freeze
   b. spread   d. melt

4. A person who has boasted to friends has _____.
   a. bragged   c. complained
   b. run   d. dragged

5. An elephant's tusks are two of its _____.
   a. tears   c. food
   b. helpers   d. teeth

6. When people are whittling, they are _____.
   a. sunning   c. carving
   b. curving   d. starting

7. Something that has commenced has already _____.
   a. finished   c. begun
   b. become   d. flown

Books to Read

Bond, Michael *Tales of Olga da Polga*

Olga da Polga is a guinea pig who is bought by Karen and her parents. Olga is a talented storyteller and entertains her animal friends with stories of the adventures of her favorite animals, guinea pigs.

Bunting, Eve *The Big Find*

Yashi's grandfather uses cormorant birds to catch the fish that they sell. They worry about catching enough fish to be able to keep their boat.

Howe, Deborah *Bunnicula, A Rabbit-Tale of Mystery*

Chester, the cat, knows that the new little rabbit is behind the strange events happening in the house, but convincing anyone proves to be a real challenge.

McGovern, Ann *True Adventures of Eugenie Clark: Shark Lady*

Eugenie Clark's interest in fish began when she saw the fish in the tanks at the New York Zoo. She has established a marine biology lab in Florida and today is a college professor. She travels around the world to study the life of the oceans.

North, Sterling *Rascal*

In this autobiographical story, Sterling North tells of his pet, a mischievous raccoon. During the year that North was eleven years old, he and the raccoon had many great adventures.

ACHIEVEMENTS

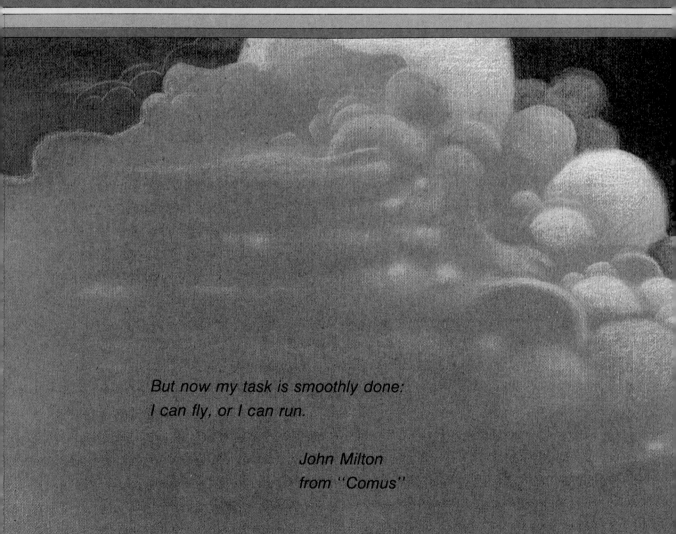

But now my task is smoothly done:
I can fly, or I can run.

John Milton
from "Comus"

385

The Muffin Muncher

Stephen Cosgrove

Problems often can be solved by people working together. The king and villagers of a very poor castle have a problem: a monstrous muffin-munching dragon. A solution is needed. As you read this story, you will see how working hand in hand can be exactly what is needed to solve problems for kings and dragons as well as for people.

Many, many years ago in the far corner of a very poor country stood the poorest of poor castles.

The villagers of the castle did not have riches and valuables. They were also poor in spirit. They had done nothing to be proud of.

The only way they had stayed alive at all was by baking and selling the best muffins in the land.

Every morning the king, who was also the head baker, would bake a fresh batch. When he had finished, the people would load their carts and set off for the other villages in the kingdom.

There was never any trouble selling the muffins. They were the finest ever baked. But because the people were so poor, they had to use all the money they had earned to buy wood for the fire and flour to make more.

So, day in and day out, the head baker, who was also

the king, would build up the giant fires in the ovens and
bake muffins.

He would slowly mix all the ingredients in a big
cracked bowl. Then he would pour the mix into the tins
and put them in the ovens to bake.

The people were just barely getting along. As if things
were not bad enough, there appeared at the castle one day
a great dragon. Now, this was not your everyday, run-of-
the-mill dragon. He was rather large. He was a little
heavy. He was a muffin-munching dragon.

With crumbs still on his face from the last muffins he'd
eaten, he came down the hill, right up to the bridge.

Taking one look, the people ran over the bridge and
into the castle.

The dragon took a great long smell. He said, "I smell muffins!" This castle, he decided, smelled like a nice place to stay. He moved in, right under the bridge.

He was very tired from his long journey. So he took his pillow and the picture of his pony from his bag, curled up, and fell fast asleep.

The next morning the people looked out their castle windows and thought that the dragon was gone. Breathing a sigh, they began preparing for another day.

After loading their wagons with fresh warm muffins, they set off across the bridge, over the soundly sleeping dragon. With all the noise from the wagons, he woke up.

He peeked over the edge to see what was going on. "So, that's it. Those muffins look so good and I am very hungry."

He thought and thought and finally came up with a plan. He jumped up on the bridge right in front of the people, tried to look very mean, and roared. "Stop, or I shall knock down your bridge!" Then he blew a little flame and puffed three smoke rings.

"From now on," he rumbled, "you shall each give me ten of your best muffins as your price to cross my bridge."

"But this is our bridge!" they cried.

"Well, if I knock it down, it won't be anybody's bridge," said the dragon.

The people thought and talked awhile and finally agreed to give the dragon what he wanted. They barely had enough money to buy wood, let alone enough money to build a new bridge.

From then on, every wagon that crossed the bridge left

ten muffins. With crumbs all around him, the dragon would sit there, stuffing those scrumptious muffins away.

This might have gone on to this day except for one little thing. The dragon was eating so many muffins that the people did not have enough to sell. Because of that, they didn't have enough money to buy wood for the ovens or even flour to bake more.

They would return every day with fewer goods. One day they all came home with nothing.

The next morning the head baker, who was also the king, could not fire up the great ovens because there was no wood. He could not use his big cracked bowl because he had no flour or goods to put in it.

With a heavy heart and a tear in his eye, the baker sat sadly on a pile of empty flour sacks and cried. "We have no more goods to make muffins. Our bridge will be knocked down. What are we ever to do?"

That same day the dragon woke up, brushed his teeth, combed his hair, and prepared for another day of munching.

He waited and waited and waited. No wagons came. His stomach began to rumble and roar. He tried eating a few of the crumbs that had dropped on the ground the day before. They were stale. "No muffins?" he roared.

Finally he decided to enter the castle and find out what had happened to all his muffins.

The dragon walked through the castle until he reached the bakery. Then he peeked inside. "Where are my muffins?" he roared. "I've been waiting and waiting and waiting! Where are they?"

The head baker, who was also the king, walked up to the dragon as bravely as he could. "Mr. Dragon," he said, "we are poor people. We live in a poor castle which has very little. Before you came, the muffins we sold barely paid for our wood and goods to mix. Now that we have to give you so many muffins, we can't buy enough wood. Our ovens have no heat."

That poor dragon was so very confused. He wanted some muffins because he was so hungry. But at the same time he felt sorry for the baker and the other people who lived in the castle.

He thought and thought. Finally, a great big smile crossed his face. "I have it!" he shouted. He asked the head baker, who was also the king, to call all the people to a castle meeting so that he could tell them of his wonderful plan.

The people happily began to cheer and shout as he finished. Surely the dragon had solved the castle's problems, and his own.

Then and for always, the dragon heated the ovens of the bakery with his mighty flame. With the extra money they saved by not having to buy wood, the people were able to leave a stack of muffins in reach of the muffin-munching dragon.

While heating up the ovens
With a lot of style and grace,
The muffin muncher smiles a smile
With crumbs upon his face.

Answer these questions.

1. Where did this story take place?

2. How were the villagers of the castle able to make a living?

3. What did the villagers do with the money they earned from selling muffins?

4. What did the dragon do to get muffins from the villagers?

5. What happened in the village as the dragon ate more and more muffins?

6. Why was the dragon's solution to the villagers' problem a wise one?

Running with Rachel

Frank and Jan Asch

People do exercises every day. This story is about a girl named Rachel. Rachel learns a new kind of exercise, running. This story gives some tips that runners should keep in mind when they run.

One day I was riding my bike and I saw a woman running down the road. She was wearing bright blue shorts with a stripe down the side, funny green sneakers, and heavy socks. I turned to look. Then I skidded on some loose gravel.

I went flying over the handlebars and landed in a ditch. I wasn't hurt much, just scraped up a bit. My bike wasn't so lucky. The front wheel was bent out of shape. It was impossible to ride home. I could hardly push it. Then the woman in the bright blue shorts came over to me.

"Hey, are you okay?" she asked.

"I guess so. But look at my bike!"

"Can I give you a hand with it?"

"Sure," I said. She helped me push the bike all the way home.

"What's your name?" she asked.

"Rachel," I said. "What's yours?"

"Cathy," she replied.

Cathy was very easy to talk to. I told her about my doll-house collection and my guinea pigs. She told me about her new job and vegetable garden. And of course I wanted to know why she'd been running down the road!

When we got to my house, my dog came to greet us. Cathy knelt down to pet him and got licked in the face.

"I'll bet you get chased by a lot of dogs," I said.

"It happens sometimes," she replied. "The little ones I tell to go home in a firm voice. The big ones I try to ignore."

"And what if that doesn't work?" I asked.

"Then," she said, smiling, "I run a little faster."

My mom met Cathy. She offered her a glass of water. We talked some more, mostly about running. I had a lot of questions. Cathy didn't mind answering them.

"How did you get started?" I asked.

"I bought myself a good pair of running shoes," she said, "and just started running. I began with a quarter mile. Then I built up slowly to give my body a chance to get used to it. In a few weeks I was up to a mile. Now it's been several months. I run at least three miles a day."

"Isn't there more to it than just having a good pair of running shoes?" asked my mother.

"Well," said Cathy, "there are some simple things to remember. Don't run right after you eat. Also, do a few warm-up exercises so you don't hurt yourself. Another thing that's important is to use your whole foot when you run. You should land on your heel, roll to the ball of your foot, and push off with your toes. What that does is help distribute the shock evenly and prevent knee injuries."

"And that's it?" asked my mom.

"Really, if you're just running for the fun of it, it's not that hard. But of course if you're overweight or think there might be some medical trouble, you should see your doctor before you begin."

"Running's not for me," said my mom. "I like accomplishing something when I exercise, like working in the garden."

"Oh, you have a garden?" exclaimed Cathy. "So do I."

My mom loves to show off her garden. That was the last I saw of them until Cathy had to leave.

"Thanks a lot for helping me with my bike," I shouted after her.

"See you around," she said as she jogged down the road.

A Trial Run

I've always liked running. Whenever I have a choice between running and walking, like to the store for my mom or just from the front door to the school bus, I always choose running. Walking takes too much time. Running just feels better.

Later that week I got home from school a bit frazzled. I turned on the TV but there was nothing interesting on. My mind was racing around in five different directions. My body felt like a lump. I felt itchy—but on the inside!

I decided to go for a run.

I ran out the front door, down the drive, and up the street. At the corner I ran across the baseball field and around the pond where a few kids were fishing. Then I ran away from all the houses and into the fields. It was the end of May. Lots of flowers were already blooming. I felt my heart pounding and the blood rushing through my veins. Everything in my body was saying:

"Hey, where have you been all day? We missed you."

My shadow ran along with me. It fell across the new green grass that was growing redder as the sun set. I ran the way Cathy had shown me, rolling forward from my heel to my toe. I still had on my school shoes. They were starting to hurt.

I looked down at my shadow. It seemed alive to me. I wondered if I could stop suddenly and catch it off guard. Would it run ahead a few paces? I picked up a little more speed. I pretended that I could outrun my shadow.

By now my feet were really hurting. I slowed down to a jog and then to a walk. My heart was still pounding. My arms and legs felt tingly, like blood was flowing to places it had never gone before.

I sat down and took my shoes off to see what the damages were.

"Congratulations!" I told myself. "You are the proud mother of several baby blisters."

My feet hurt. I knew I could get good shoes and take care of that. What mattered was that that itchy-on-the-inside feeling was gone now.

I limped home. I wondered how Mom was going to take the news that I needed a new pair of shoes—running shoes.

Running Shoes

Mom took the news just fine. In fact, a few days later we went downtown to buy my first pair of running shoes.

"What you should look for in a jogging shoe," the sales clerk said, "is a sole that's padded and bends easily. It should have a heel that is somewhat raised—about the same as a street shoe."

Mom insisted that they have good arch supports. The sales clerk agreed.

I tried on a few pairs. The first pair was so heavy it made me feel like Bigfoot. The next pair was nice and light. However, they were too tight in the toes. The third pair seemed to fit better.

"It's important that they feel comfortable," said the sales clerk.

Mom helped me lace up the shoes. I jogged up and down the aisle of the store.

"They feel very comfortable," I said.

"Good," said the sales clerk. She put my old shoes in a box. We went to the front to pay for the new shoes.

"I'll meet you at the car," I yelled to Mom. Then I took off down the street like a pebble from a slingshot.

My new shoes really made me feel important, and somehow a better, faster runner. My feet felt so light and sure as they gripped the pavement. I tried to use my whole foot the way Cathy had said. It felt great. I leaped up and down curbs. I stopped on a dime at the traffic light. I knew it would take my mom a while to pay the bill and walk to the car. I decided to take the long route.

As I ran through the park, the squirrels picked up their heads. I could see and feel springtime all around.

When I got to the car Mom was already there.

That night I wrote in my diary.

Dear Diary,

Today I got my first pair of running shoes. They're blue and white. They're so soft they make my feet feel like they're wrapped in clouds. They were kind of expensive. But Mom wanted to get me good ones. She didn't say anything. However, I can tell she's afraid I'll lose interest in running. Then they will be just so much wasted money. I don't think she has to worry. I like running as much as my dollhouse and my guinea pigs, too!

Yippie!!!

More Tips from Cathy

The next day was Saturday. I got up early. I put on my new shoes and shorts and went for a run. I was hoping to see Cathy again. I ran back and forth past the spot where we first met. At last she came running down the road. She seemed as pleased to see me as I was to see her.

We sat down on the grass and talked for a while. She wanted to hear everything about my new interest in running. Then she offered to show me some warm-up exercises.

"I always start with some leg stretching. Bend your standing leg and put the other leg back. Keep your knee straight. Lean forward a little. Put your weight on the leg that's bent."

"Like this?" I asked. *(See Diagram A.)*

"Good. Now switch legs."

I could feel my muscles stretching like a new rubber band.

Diagram A

"Boy, did I need that," I said.

"Be careful not to strain," warned Cathy.

"I see what you mean about certain places needing exercise more than others. That one is hard for me!"

"Leg-stretching exercises are very important," Cathy told me. "That's because running puts so much strain on the legs."

"What's next?" I asked.

"Forward bending. Just bend at the waist. Try to touch your toes."

I could touch my toes right away. Then I stretched a little more and touched the ground with my fingers, then with the palms of my hands. It didn't hurt at all. *(See Diagram B.)*

"That one's easier," I said.

Diagram B

Diagram C

Next we did some trunk twisting. *(See Diagram C.)* Trunk twisting was the easiest of all. It made my back feel really good.

"What about sit-ups, jumping jacks, and all of the ones that we do in gym?" I asked.

"Those are good, too," said Cathy. "Just try them all. Soon you'll find the ones that suit you best."

After ten or fifteen minutes of working out we were almost ready to run. First I asked Cathy to give me a few tips on form.

"Just remember to keep your back more or less straight. Keep your shoulders level. Don't hunch over. Your lungs will be able to expand more that way. Keep your forearms level with the ground and your hands loosely clenched. No fists."

I laughed. "Do you really think I can remember all that?"

"No," she said, "you'll go crazy. You'll end up hating running if you try to get everything right the first time. Just think about one thing at a time. Let your body put it all together for you."

Now we were ready to run. I wanted to go fast right away but Cathy said that we start out slowly and build up. Every once in a while she looked over at me.

"You're making fists," she said. "Relax your hands!"

I imitated her motion, flicking my wrists like limp rags while I ran.

"That's it," she said. "Now you've got it."

After a while we built up speed. We ran for half a mile or so. Then she walked me the rest of the way home.

"You should always do some sort of warm-down. That way you won't stiffen up after a run," she said. "Walking is good. You could even try some of the same exercises I showed you before."

As we said good-bye, Cathy asked me how I liked my first running lesson. I told her I'd really enjoyed it and thanked her for all the tips. We agreed to get together again sometime.

Since that day I've run many times. I've run in races. Best of all, I made a friend my own age who also likes to run.

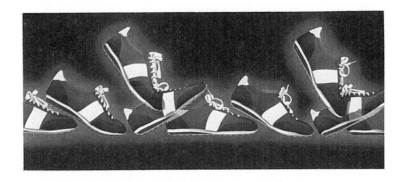

Answer these questions.

1. What was Cathy doing when Rachel first saw her?

2. Why does Rachel prefer running over walking?

3. What happened to Rachel's feet when she ran in her school shoes? What took care of this problem?

4. What should the sole and the heel of a running shoe be like?

5. Why was Cathy so concerned with the kind of shoes that Rachel's mom had bought for her and with all the warm-up exercises?

6. What has happened to Rachel since she has begun running?

Reading in Science

Use your paper to complete the exercise below.

1. Look at the selection. What is the selection about?
2. Are there heads or subheads? What are they? What will each section be about?
3. Are any words in boldface or italic type? List them.
4. Skim the material and make a list of words that are unfamiliar to you. Write the meanings of these words by using clues in the sentence or a dictionary.
5. Read the selection. List the important details.
6. In your own words write a paragraph that summarizes the information in the selection. If possible, use the words that you listed as unfamiliar or use synonyms for these words.

Tornadoes

A spring wind that brushes your cheek can whirl into *vicious,* or violent, storms called tornadoes. Tornadoes have been known to peel bark from trees and to explode buildings. Tornadoes have also been known to do some even stranger things. One time a tornado carried a crate of eggs for 500 yards (457 meters). It set the crate down very gently and did not break even one egg.

How Tornadoes Are Formed

Warm air is light in weight. Cool air is much heavier. Tornadoes are formed when places are surrounded by warm, moist air. A mass of cool air moves into the area on top of the warm, moist air. The warm air is then unable to move or rise. Dark thunderstorm clouds gather in the sky. The warm air swirls until it finds a weak spot in the cool air above it. It rushes to the spot and the cool air follows. The dark clouds begin to swirl. They may turn dark green or black. Heavy rain and lightning may begin. A long taillike cloud may spin toward the earth. Some never touch the ground. It may look like an elephant's trunk whipping back and forth. These kinds of tornadoes make hissing noises when they pass overhead. Sometimes these tails do reach the earth. These tornadoes then travel along the ground. They make a loud roaring sound and may destroy everything in their path.

Eleanor Roosevelt

Cynthia Mellizo

People find many things frightening. Some people find ways to overcome their fears. Eleanor Roosevelt was the wife of Franklin Delano Roosevelt, president of the United States from 1933 to 1945. This biography tells how Eleanor overcame her fears and became one of the most famous people of the twentieth century.

As a young girl, Eleanor was afraid of horses. However, she was determined to learn to ride. She worked every day. At the end of each day she found that she was a little less afraid of horses. Soon she had learned to ride well. She had also lost her fear of horses.

Eleanor had learned a great lesson. People can do many things that at first seem scary. They just have to believe in themselves. They must also not show that they are afraid. By keeping in mind what she had learned, Eleanor Roosevelt did many great things during her life.

One of the worst times that Eleanor had to face was when her husband, Franklin, became very ill. Franklin went sailing one day while his family was staying at their summer home on Campobello Island in Canada. He became very ill. The doctors decided that he had polio. They said that he would live but that he would never be able to use his legs again.

By wearing leg braces and using crutches, Franklin hoped that he would not always have to stay in a wheelchair. He hoped that he would be able to go almost anyplace and be able to do almost anything that he wished. He would exercise to make his arms strong so that he could use the crutches he would need. With Eleanor's help, Franklin made his hopes reality.

Franklin wanted a life in politics. He had been in the New York state senate. He had been one of the people in charge of the Navy Department in Washington, D.C. Now his time would be spent in making himself strong. However, Franklin and Eleanor were worried that the people would forget about his work. Eleanor went to all of the places that Franklin could not visit and made speeches for him. For someone as shy as Eleanor, this was very hard to do. However, when Eleanor thought about what she had learned about being afraid, she gained the strength she needed to make the speeches. Franklin was chosen to be the governor of New York, and then he became the president of the United States. Eleanor became the first lady of the land.

Franklin became president while the Depression was still raging. Many people had little to eat and were poor. Millions of people did not have jobs. Franklin had so much work to do that he could not take the time to make many visits. Eleanor made visits for him. She visited people in homes, in the coal mines where they worked, in hospitals, in schools, and in

other places, where she could find out what was happening. She made reports to Franklin, and he worked to change those things she had found that were bad. He also praised those things she had found that were great. Together they spent their years in the White House trying to make life better for all people.

During the time that Franklin was the president, the United States fought World War II. Eleanor flew all over the world to meet with America's soldiers and friends in other countries. A few months before the war was won, Franklin died. Eleanor was alone.

Harry Truman asked Eleanor to help make one of Franklin's dreams come true. Franklin had hoped that all of the countries would form a worldwide group. The group would work to solve the world's problems without war. It was to be the United Nations. Eleanor became a member of the team

America sent to help form the group. By the time that Eleanor's work was done, the United Nations had been formed and was housed in a new building in New York City.

Many times during her life Eleanor had been afraid. She remembered the lesson that she had learned and often thought of Franklin. She remembered the speech he made when he first became president. In that speech he had said, "There is nothing to fear but fear itself."

Eleanor put aside her fears and was an inspiration to many people.

Answer these questions.

1. What great lesson did Eleanor Roosevelt learn as she practiced riding horses?

2. What did Eleanor do for Franklin as he worked to become strong enough to move around with crutches?

3. How did Eleanor and Franklin spend their years in the White House?

4. What did Eleanor do to help make one of Franklin's dreams come true? Who asked her to do this work?

5. What had Franklin once said that had helped Eleanor overcome her fears?

6. Why would Eleanor do so many things of which she was afraid?

Write on your own.

The White House has a swimming pool, a bowling alley, a movie theater, and many other features for the president and the first lady's use. Write three questions that you would like to have answered about the White House, about what it is like living there, or about the president and the first lady.

The Southpaw

Judith Viorst

Everyone needs friends, but sometimes remaining friends can be a little difficult. Richard and Janet used to be friends. Read ''The Southpaw'' to find out how they become friends all over again.

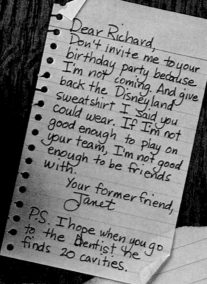

Dear Richard,
Don't invite me to your birthday party because I'm not coming. And give back the Disneyland sweatshirt I said you could wear. If I'm not good enough to play on your team, I'm not good enough to be friends with.

Your former friend,
Janet

P.S. I hope when you go to the Dentist he finds 20 cavities.

Dear Janet,

Here is your stupid Disneyland sweatshirt, if that's how you're going to be. I want my comic books now — finished or not. No girl has ever played on the Mapes Street baseball team, and as long as I'm captain, no girl ever will.

Your former friend,

Richard

P.S. I hope when you go for your checkup you need a tetanus shot.

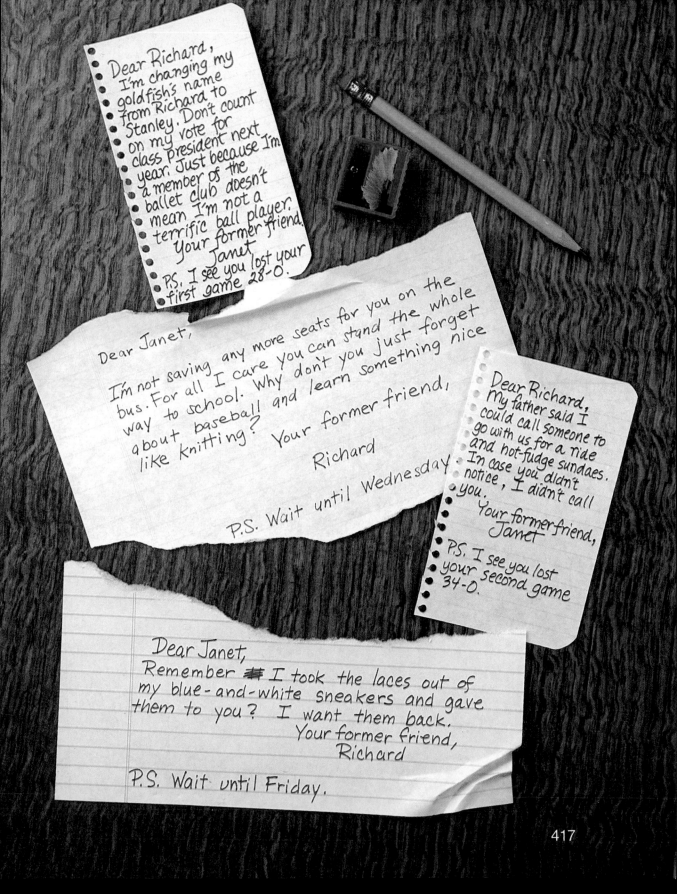

417

Dear Richard,
Congratulations on your unbroken record. Eight straight losses, wow! I understand you're the laughing-stock of New Jersey.
Your former friend,
Janet

P.S. Why don't you and your team forget about baseball and learn something nice like knitting maybe?

Dear Janet,

Here's the silver horseback riding trophy that you gave me. I don't think I want to keep it anymore.
Your former friend,
Richard

P.S. I didn't think you'd be the kind who'd kick a man when he's down.

Dear Richard,
I wasn't kicking exactly. I was kicking back.
Your former friend,
Janet

P.S. In case you were wondering, my batting average is .345.

Dear Janet,

Alfie is having his tonsils out tomorrow. We might be able to let you catch next week.

Richard

418

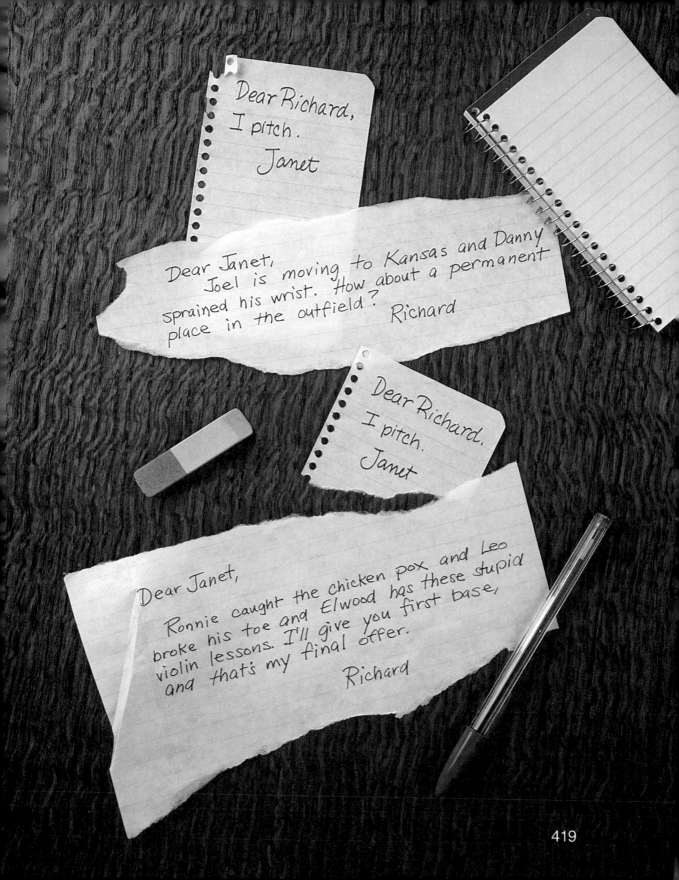

419

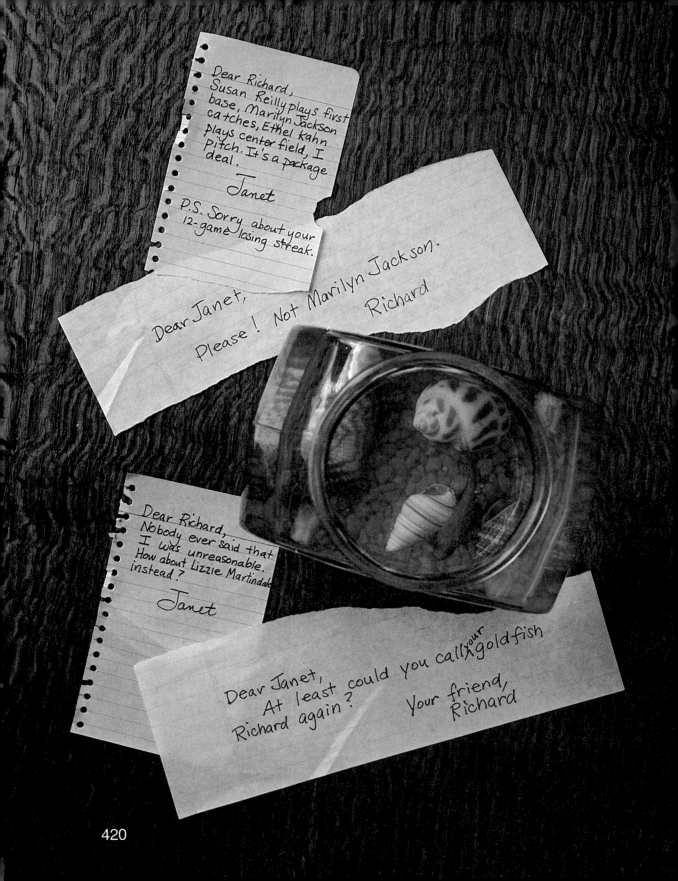

Dear Richard,
Susan Reilly plays first base, Marilyn Jackson catches, Ethel Kahn plays center field, I pitch. It's a package deal.

Janet

P.S. Sorry about your 12-game losing streak.

Dear Janet,
Please! Not Marilyn Jackson.

Richard

Dear Richard,
Nobody ever said that I was unreasonable. How about Lizzie Martindale instead?

Janet

Dear Janet,
At least could you call your goldfish Richard again?

Your friend,
Richard

420

Answer these questions.

1. What caused an argument between Janet and Richard?

2. What information did Janet include in her notes to suggest to Richard that the team needed her?

3. Why was Janet at first unwilling to play on Richard's team, even when he offered her a position?

4. What package deal did Janet offer Richard?

5. How did Janet and Richard reach an agreement?

6. What kind of friends had Richard and Janet been before the argument? How do you know?

About the Author

An author of many children's books, Judith Viorst writes mainly for or about her own children. When her son Nicholas was continually being teased by his older brother Anthony, she wrote *I'll Fix Anthony* to make Nicholas feel better. She wrote *My Mama Says There Aren't Any Zombies, Ghosts, Vampires, Creatures, Demons, Monsters, Fiends, Goblins, or Things* also for Nicholas when he was young and afraid of monsters.

Using a Telephone Book

Names in a telephone book are listed in alphabetical order according to the people's last names. Many people have the same last name. A reader must find the last name and then look for the person's first name. These are listed in alphabetical order, too. Addresses are listed beside each name.

A. Use your own paper and this list from the phone book to answer the following questions.

LEEK Thomas 4503 SE 28th. 555-7516

LEMASTER LJ 163 Royal Rd. 555-4867

LEMON Alan 927 W. Park Pl. 555-3552

LEMONS Laura 1117 Pecan. 555-5425

LESTER RD 224 Walker. 555-5022

   Stephen 654 Hill. 555-0918

LEWIS Barbara 915 NE 32. 555-1057

1. To call Laura Lemons, what number would you dial?
2. Where does L. J. Lemaster live?
3. How many people named Lester are listed?

The Yellow Pages of a telephone book list the telephone numbers of the people and companies that sell things or provide services for a community. If you need to find something special, look in the Yellow Pages. All the names of people and companies included in the Yellow Pages are listed in alphabetical order. However, they are grouped under headings that tell what they sell or the services that they provide.

B. Use the following example of the Yellow Pages and your own paper to answer the questions.

> **Electric Motors**
> Daytone Motors 1769 NE 56th 555-9876
> **Elevators**
> Dell Elevators 162 SE 16th 555-9584
> Handicapped Aids 635 Myrtle 555-1113

1. What number can be called to find someone to fix an electric motor?
2. Which company carries elevators for the handicapped?

Emergency numbers are usually listed in the front of a telephone book.

C. Use the following example of the emergency numbers page and your own paper to answer the questions.

> *Emergency Numbers*
> *Fire* - 555-5678 . . . . nonemergency - 555-3113
> *Police* - 555-6931 . . . . nonemergency - 555-8591
> *Ambulance* - 555-9375 . . . . nonemergency - 555-0285

1. What number should be called to report smoke seen coming out of a neighbor's house?
2. What number should be called to ask that an ambulance be sent to the scene of an emergency?

Escape

E. B. White

Wilbur was the smallest of the baby pigs born on the farm where a girl named Fern lived. Fern's parents allowed her to care for Wilbur until he was large enough to be sold. Wilbur was sold to the Zuckermans, and he now lives in their barnyard. Fern still visits him every day. In ''Escape'' Wilbur decides to leave the safety of his new home. This chapter from the book **Charlotte's Web** tells what Wilbur learns when he escapes.

One afternoon in June, when Wilbur was almost two months old, he wandered out into his small yard outside the barn. Fern had not arrived for her usual visit. Wilbur stood in the sun feeling lonely and bored.

"There's never anything to do around here," he thought. He walked slowly to his food trough and sniffed to see if anything had been overlooked at lunch. He found a small strip of potato skin and ate it. His back itched, so he leaned against the fence and rubbed against the boards. When he tired of this, he walked indoors, climbed to the top of the manure pile, and sat down. He didn't feel like going to sleep, he didn't feel like digging, he was tired of standing still, tired of lying down. "I'm less than two months old and I'm tired of living," he said. He walked out to the yard again.

"When I'm out here," he said, "there's no place to go but in. When I'm indoors, there's no place to go but out in the yard."

"That's where you're wrong, my friend, my friend," said a voice.

Wilbur looked through a fence and saw the goose standing there.

"You don't have to stay in that dirty-little dirty-little dirty-little yard," said the goose, who talked rather fast. "One of the boards is loose. Push on it, push-push-push on it, and come on out!"

"What?" said Wilbur. "Say it slower!"

"At-at-at, at the risk of repeating myself," said the goose, "I suggest that you come on out. It's wonderful out here."

"Did you say a board was loose?"

Wilbur walked up to the fence and saw that the goose was right—one board was loose. He put his head down, shut his eyes, and pushed. The board gave way. In a minute he had squeezed through the fence and was standing in the long grass outside his yard. The goose chuckled.

"How does it feel to be free?" she asked.

"I like it," said Wilbur. "That is, I *guess* I like it." Actually, Wilbur felt queer to be outside his fence, with nothing between him and the big world.

"Where do you think I'd better go?"

"Anywhere you like, anywhere you like," said the goose. "Go down through the orchard, root up the sod! Go down through the garden, dig up the radishes! Root up everything! Eat grass! Look for corn! Look for oats! Run all over! Skip and dance, jump and prance! Go down through the orchard and stroll in the woods! The world is a wonderful place when you're young."

"I can see that," replied Wilbur. He gave a jump in the air, twirled, ran a few steps, stopped, looked all around, sniffed the smells of afternoon, and then set off walking down through the orchard. Pausing in the shade of an apple tree, he put his strong snout into the ground and began pushing, digging, and rooting. He felt very happy.

He had plowed up quite a piece of ground before anyone noticed him. Mrs. Zuckerman was the first to see him. She saw him from the kitchen window, and she immediately shouted for the men.

"Ho-*mer!*" she cried. "Pig's out! Lurvy! Pig's out! Homer! Lurvy! Pig's out. He's down there under that apple tree."

"Now the trouble starts," thought Wilbur. "Now I'll catch it."

The goose heard the racket and she, too, started hollering. "Run-run-run downhill, make for the woods, the woods!" she shouted to Wilbur. "They'll never-never-never catch you in the woods."

The cocker spaniel heard the commotion and he ran out from the barn to join the chase. Mr. Zuckerman heard, and he came out of the machine shed where he was mending a tool. Lurvy, the hired man, heard the noise and came up from the asparagus patch where he was pulling weeds. Everybody walked toward Wilbur and Wilbur didn't know what to do. The woods seemed a long way off, and anyway, he had never been down there in the woods and wasn't sure he would like it.

"Get around behind him, Lurvy," said Mr. Zuckerman, "and drive him toward the barn! And take it easy— don't rush him! I'll go and get a bucket of slops."

The news of Wilbur's escape spread rapidly among the animals on the place. Whenever any creature broke loose on Zuckerman's farm, the event was of great interest to the others. The goose shouted to the nearest cow that Wilbur was free, and soon all the cows knew. Then one of the cows told one of the sheep, and soon all the sheep knew. The lambs learned about it from their mothers. The horses, in their stalls in the barn, pricked up their ears when they heard the goose hollering; and soon the horses had caught on to what was happening. "Wilbur's out," they said. Every animal stirred and lifted its head and became excited to know that one of his friends had got free and was no longer penned up or tied fast.

Wilbur didn't know what to do or which way to run. It seemed as though everybody was after him. "If this is what it's like to be free," he thought, "I believe I'd rather be penned up in my own yard."

The cocker spaniel was sneaking up on him from one side. Lurvy the hired man was sneaking up on him from the other side. Mrs. Zuckerman stood ready to head him off if he started for the garden. Now Mr. Zuckerman was coming down toward him carrying a pail. "This is really awful," thought Wilbur. "Why doesn't Fern come?" He began to cry.

The goose took command and began to give orders.

"Don't just stand there, Wilbur! Dodge about, dodge about!" cried the goose. "Skip around, run toward me, slip in and out, in and out, in and out! Make for the woods! Twist and turn!"

The cocker spaniel sprang for Wilbur's hind leg. Wilbur jumped and ran. Lurvy reached out and grabbed. Mrs. Zuckerman screamed at Lurvy. The goose cheered for Wilbur. Wilbur dodged between Lurvy's legs. Lurvy missed Wilbur and grabbed the spaniel instead. "Nicely done, nicely done!" cried the goose. "Try it again, try it again!"

"Run downhill!" suggested the cows.

"Run toward me!" yelled the gander.

"Run uphill!" cried the sheep.

"Turn and twist!" honked the goose.

"Jump and dance!" said the rooster.

"Look out for Lurvy!" called the cows.

"Look out for Zuckerman!" yelled the gander.

"Watch out for the dog!" cried the sheep.

"Listen to me, listen to me!" screamed the goose.

Poor Wilbur was dazed and frightened by this hullabaloo. He didn't like being the center of all this fuss. He tried to follow the instructions his friends were giving him, but he couldn't run downhill and uphill at the same time. He couldn't turn and twist when he was jumping and dancing. He was crying so hard he could barely see anything that was happening. After all, Wilbur was a very young pig—not much more than a baby, really. He wished Fern were there to take him in her arms and comfort him.

When he looked up and saw Mr. Zuckerman standing quite close to him, holding a pail of warm slops, he felt relieved. He lifted his nose and sniffed. The smell was delicious—warm milk, potato skins, wheat middlings, Kellogg's Corn Flakes, and a popover left from the Zuckermans' breakfast.

"Come, pig!" said Mr. Zuckerman, tapping the pail. "Come pig!"

Wilbur took a step toward the pail.

"No-no-no!" said the goose. "It's the old pail trick, Wilbur. Don't fall for it, don't fall for it! He's trying to lure you back into captivity-ivity. He's appealing to your stomach."

Wilbur didn't care. The food smelled appetizing. He took another step toward the pail.

"Pig, pig!" said Mr. Zuckerman in a kind voice, and began walking slowly toward the barnyard, looking all about him innocently, as if he didn't know that a little white pig was following along behind him.

"You'll be sorry-sorry-sorry," called the goose.

Wilbur didn't care. He kept walking toward the pail of slops.

"You'll miss your freedom," honked the goose. "An hour of freedom is worth a barrel of slops."

Wilbur didn't care.

When Mr. Zuckerman reached the pigpen, he climbed over the fence and poured the slops into the trough. Then he pulled the loose board away from the fence, so that there was a wide hole for Wilbur to walk through.

"Reconsider, reconsider!" cried the goose.

Wilbur paid no attention. He stepped through the fence into his yard. He walked to the trough and took a long drink of slops, sucking in the milk hungrily and chewing the popover. It was good to be home again.

While Wilbur ate, Lurvy fetched a hammer and some 8-penny nails and nailed the board in place. Then he and Mr. Zuckerman leaned lazily on the fence and Mr. Zuckerman scratched Wilbur's back with a stick.

"He's quite a pig," said Lurvy.

"Yes, he'll make a good pig," said Mr. Zuckerman.

Wilbur heard the words of praise. He felt the warm milk inside his stomach. He felt the pleasant rubbing of the stick along his itchy back. He felt peaceful and happy and sleepy. This had been a tiring afternoon. It was still only about four o'clock but Wilbur was ready for bed.

"I'm really too young to go out into the world alone," he thought as he lay down.

About the Author

E. B. White was born in 1899 in Mount Vernon, New York. He wrote the book *Charlotte's Web.* It was published in 1952 after he began living on a farm in Maine. He liked farm life, especially the animals. The idea for Charlotte, Wilbur's spider friend, came when White found a spider that was about to become a mother. He was fascinated with the spider and kept a close watch on her. He even cut down the spider and sac from their web, put them in a box, and took them with him when he went on an out-of-town trip.

Answer these questions.

1. Where did Wilbur live?

2. Who talked Wilbur into leaving the barnyard?

3. Who was the first person to see Wilbur outside his pen?

4. Who chased Wilbur around the orchard?

5. Who was finally able to get Wilbur back to his pen? How did he get Wilbur to go back?

6. Why was the goose so interested in seeing that Wilbur stay free and so upset when he went back into the pen?

Write on your own.

Wilbur liked the slops that the Zuckermans fed him. Think of an animal that might be found in the zoo. Decide what you would use to lure this animal back to its cage if it had gotten out. Write a paragraph that describes what you would do.

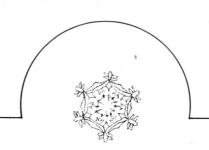

Snow can make everything look very beautiful. It can also make life very dangerous. This chapter, from the book The Long Winter, *tells about a storm that happens in the late 1800s. The snow is so heavy that people cannot even see where to go. Laura, Carrie, their teacher, and their schoolmates must try to find their way home from school.*

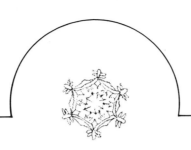

THE LONG WINTER

Laura Ingalls Wilder

Suddenly there was no sunshine. It went out, as if someone had blown out the sun like a lamp. The outdoors was gray, the windowpanes were gray, and at the same moment a wind crashed against the schoolhouse, rattling windows and doors and shaking the walls.

Miss Garland started up from her chair. One of the little Beardsley girls screamed and Carrie turned white.

Laura thought, "It happened this way on Plum Creek, the Christmas when Pa was lost." Her whole heart hoped and prayed that Pa was safe at home now.

Teacher and all the others were staring at the windows, where nothing but grayness could be seen. They all looked frightened. Then Miss Garland said, "It is only a storm, children. Go on with your lessons."

The blizzard was scouring against the walls, and the winds squealed and moaned in the stovepipe.

All the heads bent over the books as Teacher had told them to do. But Laura was trying to think how to get home. The schoolhouse was a long way from Main Street, and there was nothing to guide them.

All the others had come from the East that summer. They had never seen a prairie blizzard. But Laura and Carrie knew what it was. Carrie's head was bowed limply above her book, and the back of it, with the white parting between the braids of fine, soft hair, looked small and helpless and frightened.

There was only a little fuel at the schoolhouse. The school board was buying coal, but only one load had been delivered. Laura thought they might outlive the storm in the schoolhouse, but they could not do it without burning all the costly patent desks.

Without lifting her head Laura looked up at Teacher. Miss Garland was thinking and biting her lip. She could not decide to dismiss school because of a storm, but this storm frightened her.

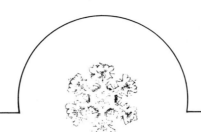

"I ought to tell her what to do," Laura thought. But she could not think what to do. It was not safe to leave the schoolhouse and it was not safe to stay there. Even the twelve patent desks might not last long enough to keep them warm until the blizzard ended. She thought of her wraps and Carrie's, in the entry. Whatever happened she must somehow keep Carrie warm. Already the cold was coming in.

There was a loud thumping in the entry. Every pupil started and looked at the door.

It opened and a man stumbled in. He was bundled in overcoat, cap, and muffler, all solid white with snow driven into the woolen cloth. They could not see who he was until he pulled down the stiffened muffler.

"I came out to get you," he told Teacher.

He was Mr. Foster, the man who owned the ox team and had come in from his claim to stay in town for the winter at Sherwood's, across the street from Teacher's house.

Miss Garland thanked him. She rapped her ruler on the desk and said, "Attention! School is dismissed. You may bring your wraps from the entry and put them on by the stove."

Laura said to Carrie, "You stay here. I'll bring your wraps."

438

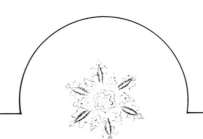

The entry was freezing cold; snow was blowing in between the rough boards of the walls. Laura was chilled before she could snatch her coat and hood from their nail. She found Carrie's and carried the armful into the schoolhouse.

Crowded around the stove, they all put on their wraps and fastened them snugly. Cap Garland did not smile. His blue eyes narrowed and his mouth set straight while Mr. Foster talked.

Laura wrapped the muffler snugly over Carrie's white face and took firm hold of her mittened hand. She told Carrie, "Don't worry, we'll be all right."

"Now, just follow me," said Mr. Foster, taking Teacher's arm. "And keep close together."

He opened the door, led the way with Miss Garland. Mary Power and Minnie each took one of the little Beardsley girls. Ben and Arthur followed them closely, then Laura went out with Carrie into blinding snow. Cap shut the door behind them.

They could hardly walk in the beating, whirling wind. The schoolhouse had disappeared. They could see nothing but swirling whiteness and snow and then a glimpse of each other, disappearing like shadows.

Laura felt that she was smothering. The icy particles

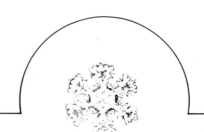

of snow whirled scratching into her eyes and smothered her breathing. Her skirts whipped around her, now wrapped so tightly that she could not step, then whirled and lifted to her knees. Suddenly tightening, they made her stumble. She held tightly to Carrie, and Carrie, struggling and staggering, was pulled away by the wind and then flung back against her.

"We can't go on this way," Laura thought. But they had to.

She was alone in the confusion of whirling winds and snow except for Carrie's hand that she must never let go. The winds struck her this way and that. She could not see nor breathe, she stumbled and was falling, then suddenly she seemed to be lifted and Carrie bumped against her. She tried to think. The others must be somewhere ahead. She must walk faster and keep up with them or she and Carrie would be lost. If they were lost on the prairie they would freeze to death.

But perhaps they were all lost. Main Street was only two blocks long. If they were going only a little way to north or south they would miss the block of stores and beyond was empty prairie for miles.

Laura thought they must have gone far enough to reach Main Street, but she could see nothing.

The storm thinned a little. She saw shadowy figures

ahead. They were darker gray in the whirling gray-whiteness. She went on as fast as she could, with Carrie, until she touched Miss Garland's coat.

They had all stopped. Huddled in their wraps, they stood like bundles close together in the swirling mist. Teacher and Mr. Foster were trying to talk, but the winds confused their shouts so that no one could hear what they said. Then Laura began to know how cold she was.

Her mittened hand was so numb that it hardly felt Carrie's hand. She was shaking all over and deep inside her there was a shaking that she could not stop. Only in her very middle there was a solid knot that ached, and her shaking pulled this knot tighter so that the ache grew worse.

She was frightened about Carrie. The cold hurt too much, Carrie could not stand it. Carrie was so little and thin, she had always been delicate, she could not stand such cold much longer. They must reach shelter soon.

Mr. Foster and Teacher were moving again, going a little to the left. All the others stirred and hurried to follow them. Laura took hold of Carrie with her other hand, that had been in her coat pocket and was not quite so numb, and then suddenly she saw a shadow go by them. She knew it was Cap Garland.

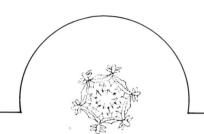

He was not following the others to the left. With hands in his pockets and head bent, he went trudging straight ahead into the storm. A fury of winds thickened the air with snow and he vanished.

Laura did not dare follow him. She must take care of Carrie and Teacher had told them to follow her. She was sure that Cap was going toward Main Street, but perhaps she was mistaken and she could not take Carrie away from the others.

She kept tight hold of Carrie and hurried to follow Mr. Foster and Teacher as fast as she could. Her chest sobbed for air and her eyes strained open in the icy snow-particles that hurt them like sand. Carrie struggled bravely, stumbling and flopping, doing her best to stay on her feet and keep going. Only for instants when the snow-whirl was thinner could they glimpse the shadows moving ahead of them.

Laura felt that they were going in the wrong direction. She did not know why she felt so. No one could see anything. There was nothing to go by—no sun, no sky, no direction in the winds blowing fiercely from all directions. There was nothing but the dizzy whirling and the cold.

It seemed that the cold and the winds, the noise of the winds and the blinding, smothering, scratching

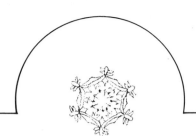

snow, and the effort and the aching, were forever. Pa had lived through three days of a blizzard under the bank of Plum Creek. But there were no creek banks here. Here there was nothing but bare prairie. Pa had told about sheep caught in a blizzard, huddled together under the snow. Some of them had lived. Perhaps people could do that, too. Carrie was too tired to go much farther, but she was too heavy for Laura to carry. They must go on as long as they could, and then . . .

Then, out of the whirling whiteness, something hit her. The hard blow crashed against her shoulder and all through her. She rocked on her feet and stumbled against something solid. It was high, it was hard, it was the corner of two walls. Her hands felt it, her eyes saw it. She had walked against some building.

With all her might she yelled, "Here! Come here! Here's a house!"

All around the house the winds were howling so that at first no one heard her. She pulled the icy stiff muffler from her mouth and screamed into the blinding storm. At last she saw a shadow in it, two tall shadows thinner than the shadowy wall she clung to—Mr. Foster and Teacher. Then other shadows pressed close around her.

No one tried to say anything. They crowded together

and they were all there—Mary Power and Minnie, each with a little Beardsley girl, and Arthur Johnson and Ben Woodworth with the small Wilmarth boys. Only Cap Garland was missing.

They followed along the side of that building till they came to the front of it, and it was Mead's Hotel, at the very north end of Main Street.

Beyond it was nothing but the railroad track covered with snow, the lonely depot and the wide, open prairie. If Laura had been only a few steps nearer the others, they would all have been lost on the endless prairie north of town.

If Laura and the others had walked on into the prairie, they might still have made it home safely. Cap Garland had found his way to Fuller's store. There he had met Laura's father. Pa had gathered a rope and a lantern and was going to search for everyone. Just as he was ready to leave, Laura and Carrie reached home.

About the Author

Laura Ingalls Wilder was an American author who was born in 1867 and died in 1957. She is best known for her nine *Little House* books for children. The books are based on events that happened as Laura grew up in the pioneer days of mid-America. The television series "Little House on the Prairie," which began in 1974, was based on her *Little House* books.

Answer these questions.

1. Why was it not safe to stay in the schoolhouse?

2. Since Laura had seen a prairie blizzard, why didn't she tell Miss Garland what to do? What does this tell about the kind of storm that it was?

3. Why did Mr. Foster come to the schoolhouse?

4. Why did Laura and Carrie fall behind the others?

5. When Laura was walking, what did she run into?

6. What would have happened if Laura had been walking nearer the others?

Poetry

Winter ice and spring rain are things that some people have never seen. Other people see more in one year than they could ever wish. However, to some people these things are wonderful. These poems describe the special feelings that one poet has about spring and another poet has about winter.

In Time of Silver Rain

In time of silver rain
The earth
Puts forth new life again,
Green grasses grow
And flowers lift their heads,
And over all the plain
The wonder spreads
    Of life,
    Of life,
    Of life!

In time of silver rain
The butterflies
Lift silken wings
To catch a rainbow cry,
And trees put forth
New leaves to sing
In joy beneath the sky
As down the roadway
Passing boys and girls
Go singing, too,
In time of silver rain
    When spring
    And life
    Are new.

Langston Hughes

448

Skating

When I try to skate,
My feet are so wary
They grit and they grate;
And then I watch Mary
Easily gliding,
Like an ice-fairy;
Skimming and curving,
Out and in,
With a turn of her head,
And a lift of her chin,
And a gleam of her eye,
And a twirl and a spin;
Sailing under
The breathless hush
Of the willows, and back
To the frozen rush;
Out to the island
And round the edge,

Skirting the rim
Of the crackling sedge,
Swerving close
To the poplar root,
And round the lake
On a single foot,
With a three, and an eight,
And a loop and a ring;
Where Mary glides,
The lake will sing!
Out in the mist
I hear her now
Under the frost
Of the willow-bough
Easily sailing,
Light and fleet,
With the song of the lake
Beneath her feet.

Herbert Asquith

Answer these questions.

1. In the poem by Langston Hughes, what happens to the earth in time of silver rain?

2. Why does Langston Hughes repeat the word **life** so often?

3. What does the narrator of "Skating" wish to be able to do?

4. What is the song of the lake?

Reading in Social Studies

Use your paper to complete the exercise below.

1. Look at the selection. What is the selection about?
2. Are there heads or subheads? What are they? What will each section be about?
3. Are any words in boldface or italic type? List them.
4. Skim the material and make a list of words that are unfamiliar to you. Write the meanings of these words by using clues in the sentence or a dictionary.
5. Read the selection. List the important details.
6. In your own words write a paragraph that summarizes the information in the selection. If possible, use the words that you listed as unfamiliar or use synonyms for these words.

The Early Egyptians and the Nile

Every spring the Nile River flooded its banks. When the flood waters withdrew, some water was left in pools and holes. The early Egyptians used this leftover water to *irrigate,* or water, their fields.

Storing Water

To store the water, they dug large holes in the earth. These holes were called catch basins. Then canals were dug from the catch basins to the fields. When the fields needed water, the Egyptian farmers opened up a side, or *lock,* in the catch basins. The water then flowed through the canals to the fields. When the catch basins were empty, the farmers refilled them with water from the Nile.

Moving Water

To make their work easier, the Egyptians invented a simple machine called the *shaduf.* The shaduf was a bucket hung from one end of a long pole. The middle of the pole was attached to the top of another post or to a tree. At the other end of the pole was a heavy stone or a clump of earth. The farmer pulled the bucket down into the water, then let it go. The stone or earth was heavier than the bucket of water. The stone would sink to the ground, raising the bucket.

Vocabulary Review

On your paper write **a, b, c,** or **d** to show the item that best completes the sentence.

1. An animal's water or food trough is a kind of _____.
   a. contact
   b. house
   c. container
   d. pasture

2. Stale bread is bread that is _____.
   a. not old
   b. not fresh
   c. not wild
   d. not fierce

3. On stairs, I keep the rails tightly clenched or _____.
   a. guarded
   b. gripped
   c. rubbed
   d. warmed

4. An ankle that was sprained was _____.
   a. twisted
   b. broken
   c. twinkled
   d. ringed

5. Reality is things that are true or that are _____.
   a. lies
   b. faces
   c. opinions
   d. facts

6. A person who has vanished has completely _____.
   a. disappeared
   b. forgotten
   c. disagreed
   d. cleaned

7. A fleet car is one that travels very _____.
   a. fast
   b. fact
   c. slowly
   d. well

Books to Read

Drury, Roger W.   *The Champion of Merrimack County*

O Crispin, the mouse, has found an antique bathtub that is the perfect place to practice for the big bicycle race. However, O Crispin has a wreck. Fixing the bicycle and getting ready for the race turns into an adventure.

Fisher, Marquita O.   *Jacqueline Cochran, First Lady of Flight*

This is a biography of Jacqueline Cochran, who during World War II helped form and also lead the Women's Airforce Service Pilots. She later became the first woman to fly faster than the speed of sound.

Peck, Robert Newton   *Trig*

Elizabeth Trigman lives in Vermont during the Great Depression of the 1930s. Known by the nickname "Trig," she wants to become an FBI agent and has many humorous adventures while investigating in her own hometown.

White, E. B.   *Charlotte's Web*

Wilbur, the pig, was lonely for the little girl who raised him and wanted a special friend. He found his friend in Charlotte, a spider. This is the story of their friendship and the special gift that Charlotte gives to Wilbur.

Wilder, Laura Ingalls   *The Long Winter*

Laura Ingalls Wilder tells the true story of her family's adventures in South Dakota during a very bad winter.

All Except Sammy

Gladys Yessayan Cretan

Everyone can do at least one thing very well. Sammy was the only one in his family who was not involved with music. A homework assignment and Sammy's keen eyesight changed his interests and helped him reach a very special goal.

Everyone in Sammy Agabashian's family was musical, except Sammy. Mama played the piano. Brother Armen played the clarinet. Sister Lucy played the cello. Papa played the violin. He was also the conductor of a whole symphony orchestra. Sammy played baseball.

Sometimes the family gave a concert together. They played many kinds of music. Usually Papa and Armen played a duet especially written for violin and clarinet. Mama and Lucy always looked beautiful up on the stage in their long silk dresses. Sammy sat in the audience and listened with the others.

When Armen or Lucy played alone, Sammy sat in front. He clapped proudly along with Papa. Sometimes the people around them shouted "Bravo!" Mama smiled happily. Everyone said, "Such a talented family. All so musical." Of course they meant everyone but Sammy.

One day a man from the newspaper came to take a picture of these musical Agabashians. He grouped them all around the piano. Mama sat at the piano bench, with her music spread in front of her. Armen stood next to her with his clarinet, ready to play. Lucy sat with her cello, the bow in position. Papa was a little to the side with his baton raised.

Then the photographer turned to Sammy. "What do you play?" he asked.

"Baseball," said Sammy.

"That's a good game. I can't put you in this picture," said the man. "This is a picture of a musical family."

So while the picture was taken, Sammy sat and watched.

Afterward he said to his mother, "I sure would like to be in the next family picture. What could I learn to play?"

"We could use another violinist," his mother said. "We'll ask Papa to give you lessons."

Papa tried. Sammy tried. It never did sound right. In fact, it sounded awful. When Sammy was playing, the cat scratched on the door to be let out. The dog hid under the bed and howled. Even Sammy's best friend, Jason, quietly rolled his eyes and went home.

"Sammy," said his father, "even for someone who is just beginning this is terrible."

"Let's try the piano," said his mother. "You need to work on your rhythm."

For days and days they worked. Sammy tried hard.

"Oh dear," said Lucy.

"Something's wrong," said Armen.

"Enough!" said his father. "Mama, the boy has no rhythm."

"Try again, Sammy," said his mother. "Listen now. One-and-two-and—no, no, no, Sammy. Can't you hear the beat?"

She sat back and shook her head. She said, "I'm afraid your father is right."

Then she had another thought. "Perhaps he will be our singer. Someday he will sing arias. Come, Sammy, what would you like to sing?"

"Take Me Out to the Ball Game," said Sammy happily.

"All right," said his mother. She started to play it on the piano. "Come," she said. "Sing out, Sammy."

Sammy tried. He knew all the words. He sang the very best he could. He sang loudly. They all listened. They all shook their heads.

"Tone-deaf," said his father. "He can't sing a note."

"How can this happen in this family?" said his mother. "Can the fruit fall so far from the tree?"

"Mama," said his father, "stop trying. It is like baking a stone. Nothing will come of it."

"Don't feel bad, Sammy," said his sister. "It doesn't matter."

"Who's feeling bad?" said Sammy.

"Come on," said his brother. "Let's go out and play ball."

"Who cares about music anyway," said Sammy.

However, Sammy really did want to be in a family picture.

After school the next day, Sammy dashed home. He ran upstairs to get his baseball bat and his mitt.

"There is a thunder in our house," said his mother.

"A thunder called Sammy," said his father. Sammy rumbled down the stairs. "Look at that black cloud on his face. Why do you frown?"

"You'd frown too," said Sammy, "if you had to go to the museum."

"No," said his mother, "I often go. It makes me happy. Why do you suddenly want to go?"

"Who wants to go?" said Sammy. "It's our homework. This week everybody has to go and find a favorite picture and tell about it."

"A good idea," said Papa.

"Listen," said Sammy, "I don't know anything about paintings. I don't even like them. How can I have a favorite?"

"Try," said his mother. "Slow down once and really look."

"One question," said his father. "Why the baseball bat?"

Sammy said, "I can't stay all day at the museum. I have baseball practice. We're up for the championship."

He walked slowly, hitting each telephone pole with his bat. At the big gray building with the tall columns in front, he stopped and wondered.

He hadn't ever gone in before.

He walked up the wide stone steps. When he came to
the great door he stopped again. He felt small. When he
stepped into the large center room with its statues and its
curving stairs and its cool marble walls, he looked around
slowly. His footsteps were very loud. A guard came up to
him. The guard told Sammy that he would have to check
his bat in the lobby.

Then Sammy climbed the stairs and wandered through
the bright rooms. There were paintings of sunflowers, of
children dressed in blue velvet, of dancers, pink on white.
Sammy gave his mitt a punch.

He passed a picture of a castle, of a golden-haired family, of a bowl of fruit shining in the sunlight. He shook his head.

When he saw a beautiful picture of small boats sailing, he stopped. That was better. After a moment he walked on. He wondered if he ever would find a real favorite.

And that is when he saw the painting of a plumed soldier sitting tall on a proud black horse.

"There!" he said. "There is a picture a person could talk about."

He stopped and looked at it for a long time. Suddenly a voice said, "Hello, Sammy!"

Sammy turned to see his friend Jason. He was standing in front of a large picture of the sea.

"Hello!" said Sammy. "Find your picture?"

"I guess I like this one," said Jason. "Looks like a big storm. What about you?"

"I'll tell about this one," Sammy said. "We'd better go now. We're late. They can't start that game without us."

The next day Sammy told his class about the picture.

"That horse could gallop and run like the wind," Sammy said.

Jason looked puzzled.

"Say!" he said later. "How could you tell how that horse could run?"

"You could see it in the picture!" said Sammy.

"Now look," said Jason, "I saw that picture. I didn't see anything like that. You even said that he had led a parade!"

"I could tell that partly from the trappings he was wearing and partly from the proud way he held his head,"

Sammy answered. "Listen, if you don't believe me, we'll stop there today on the way to the ball park. I'll show you."

"All right," said Jason. "Man," he rolled his eyes, "gallop?"

"Look," said Sammy after school. They stood in front of the picture. "Look at the power in that horse. Look at his smooth muscles. You mean to tell me that horse can't run? See how the soldier is holding the reins. He's sure of that horse. He knows he can do anything!"

After a long look, Jason shook his head. "That's a lot to tell from a painting," he said.

Sammy nodded. "It's a lot for someone to show, just with a little paint," he said.

Jason moved slowly on around the large room. Sammy sat on a bench and kept looking at the same picture. Jason tried walking in a circle on his heels. He swung his mitt around and around. He went downstairs for a drink of water. He whistled between his teeth. When he came back, Sammy still wasn't ready to go.

Jason waited and waited. "Didn't you see enough?" he asked at last.

462

"Look at this," Sammy answered.

"Same old picture," said Jason.

"I've been looking at the soldier's cape," said Sammy. "It's supposed to be red."

"Sure is red," Jason said. "Bright red."

"Yes," said Sammy, "when I first saw it I thought it was plain red. I've really been looking at it. I see that when you're close up to it, part of it is orange. Part of it is almost black. Part of it is white. When you back away from it, it all comes out red."

Jason nodded. "I suppose an artist knows how to do that," he said.

"I'd like to know how to do it too," Sammy said. "Look how he used the white and the dark to make it look like folds in the cape. Listen, that's harder to figure out than any puzzle. I'll have to come back tomorrow to look at that some more."

Jason groaned. "More?" he said.

Sammy wasn't listening. He was pointing to a sign. It was near the door. It said there was a painting class for school children on Saturday mornings.

"Look!" Sammy said. "That's for me."

"Good," said Jason. "You can ask about that red coloring. I sure was getting tired of studying it."

They walked down the wide steps and turned toward the ball field. Jason thought of something else.

"Hey!" he said. "Sammy! What about Saturday practice?"

"I'll only be a little late," Sammy said. "I wouldn't miss that."

"Sure," said Jason, "but what about Tug Smith?"

"Look," said Sammy. "We decided in the tryouts. I'm first base. He's my substitute."

"I know," said Jason. "If you don't come on Saturdays . . . Oh, oh, look. He's already standing there as if he owns first base."

Across the field they could see Tug standing with one foot on either side of first base. He saw them cutting across the field. He folded his arms. He pulled himself up tall.

"He's not planning to move," said Jason.

"Too bad," said Sammy. "Hello, Tug."

"Hi," said Tug. "They need someone in left field."

"Good," said Sammy. "Then you can still play."

"Not me," said Tug. "I'm first base."

"Since when?" said Sammy.

"Since you were late twice in a row," said Tug.

"Listen," said Sammy. "I have to be late every Saturday. You're my sub, fair enough. I was chosen first base. I'll be here as fast as I can."

"How come you'll be late?" asked Tug.

464

Sammy thought. "I have to take a class," he said.

"No school on Saturday," said Tug.

"I know," Sammy said. "This is a different kind of class. Art. At the museum."

"Art?" said Tug. "Art? Hey, guys, he's going to be a painter."

"Listen," Sammy said. "You're so smart. Can you paint a brown-black horse that looks like he can really run?"

Tug shook his head.

"Can you paint a storm at sea? Can you use orange and gray and white, and still have a cape look red?"

Tug said no.

"Neither can I," said Sammy. "That's what I'm going to try to learn. It's hard to do. Just as hard to do as playing baseball. See?"

Tug nodded. Sammy went on, "So I'll be a little late on Saturdays. You can play. Right?"

"Well," said Tug. He looked over to first base. Then he looked at all the faces around him, and back to Sammy. "Well, all right," he said.

Every Saturday Mama gave piano lessons downstairs. Armen and Lucy practiced their instruments upstairs. Papa went to work with his orchestra. Sammy went to the art class.

"What about the baseball team?" Papa asked as he walked one morning with Sammy toward the museum.

"I get there a little late," Sammy said. "The fellows don't mind because I'm painting a poster for them. We'll be the only team with our own colors and our own poster to put up whenever we're playing."

"They're lucky to have an artist on the team," said Papa. "Look at the trouble we have getting our program

covers done. Our posters for the front of the concert hall are not any better either. Either they look like a grocery list or they look like circus posters! We need a musical poster. Ah, well. Here you are. Learn well!"

Jason arrived later. Sammy was sitting quietly in front of a picture of a little girl, looking, looking.

"Studying something new?" asked Jason.

"Blue," said Sammy. "This week I'm studying blue for a new painting I started. Look," he pointed, "look at that blue dress. Part is green. Part is black. It all comes out blue."

"That's a fact," said Jason. "Never saw it that way before."

He picked up Sammy's mitt. He gave it a punch. "We get to use the big field today," he said. "Can you play late?"

"Sure," said Sammy. "There is no use going home early today, anyway. There is a man coming to take a picture of the family."

"You're in the family," said Jason.

"I know," said Sammy. "He only wants the musicians in the family. All but me."

"Never mind, Sammy," said Jason. "Maybe you can't fiddle but you sure can draw."

"That's true," said Sammy. "I can draw. I've been think-ing. Why can't I do the program cover for their concert? I'll bet I could plan a good poster. I could paint the instru-ments that they play . . . maybe in blue like in this picture . . ."

Sammy worked hard. He worked for days and days. Sometimes he painted at class. Sometimes he worked at home. While he worked he would hum, "Take me out to the ball game . . ."

"*Vagh,*" said Mama under her breath, when she heard him.

"Tone-deaf," said Papa, shaking his head.

One day Armen called, "Look! Look at Sammy's poster!"

Lucy said, "Why this is better than any we've ever had."

It was.

So this time when the picture was taken Sammy was right in the middle of the family. Sammy was holding his poster. The picture of all the Agabashians appeared in the newspaper. They were called "An Artistic Family."

"Boy!" said Sammy. "Look at that! I finally got in the picture."

"Why not?" said his father. "Must everyone play music? No. You are an artist. And a good one!"

"Not only that," said Armen, "he's a good ball player."

"Championship game tomorrow," said Lucy.

"We'll be there," said Papa Agabashian. "All of us."

The next day, there they were, sitting on the bleachers, cheering the team. There were all the talented Agabashians—except Sammy.

Sammy was at home plate, swinging his bat. He was waiting for the pitch. He felt the crack of his bat against the ball. He ran. He ran safe to first base!

He heard the yells and the whistles of the crowd. He heard the clapping and shouting of Jason and the team. He heard his family calling, "Bravo!"

"Sounds like music to me!" he said.

Rikki-Tikki-Tavi

Rudyard Kipling

This story is from a collection of stories called The Jungle
Book. *Rikki-Tikki-Tavi is a mongoose. Like all mongooses his
eyes turn a frightening red when he is angry and face to face
with his enemy.*

*At the hole where he went in
Red Eye called to Wrinkle Skin.
Hear what little Red Eye saith:
"Nag, come up and dance with death!"*

*Eye to eye and head to head
   (Keep the measure, Nag).
This shall end when one is dead
   (At thy pleasure, Nag).
Turn for turn and twist for twist
   (Run and hide thee, Nag).
Hah! The hooded Death has missed!
   (Woe betide thee, Nag!)*

This is the story of the great war that Rikki-tikki-tavi fought by himself in the big cottage in Segowlee cantonment. Darzee the Tailorbird helped him, and Chuchundra the Muskrat, who never comes out into the middle of the floor, but always creeps round by the wall, gave him helpful warnings. But Rikki-tikki did the real fighting.

He was a mongoose, rather like a little cat in his fur and his tail, but quite like a weasel in his head and his habits. His eyes and the end of his ever-moving nose were pink. He could scratch himself anywhere he pleased with any leg, front or back, that he chose to use. He could puff up his tail till it looked like a bottle brush, and his war cry as he wiggled through the long grass was: *Rikk-tikk-tikki-tikki-tchk!*

One day, a high summer flood washed him out of the groundhome where he lived with his father and mother, and carried him, kicking and clucking, down a roadside ditch. He found a little straw of grass floating there, and held to it tightly till he lost his senses. When he awakened, he was lying in the hot sun on the middle of a garden path, very bushed indeed. He heard a small boy saying, "Here's a dead mongoose. Let's have a funeral."

"No," said his mother, "let's take him in and dry him. Perhaps he isn't really dead."

They took him into the house, and a big man picked him up between his finger and thumb and said he was not dead but half choked. So they wrapped him in cotton wool, and warmed him over a little fire, and he opened his eyes and sneezed.

472

"Now," said the big man (he was an Englishman who had just moved into the cottage), "don't frighten him, and we'll see what he'll do."

It is the hardest thing in the world to frighten a mongoose, because he is eaten up from nose to tail with curiosity. The saying of all the mongoose family is "Run and find out," and Rikki-tikki was a true mongoose. He looked at the cotton wool, decided that it was not good to eat, ran all around the table, sat up and put his fur in order, scratched himself, and jumped on the small boy's shoulder.

"Don't be frightened, Teddy," said his father. "That's his way of making friends."

"Ouch! He's tickling under my chin," said Teddy.

Rikki-tikki looked down between the boy's collar and neck, snuffed at his ear, and climbed down to the floor, where he sat rubbing his nose.

"Good gracious," said Teddy's mother, "and that's a wild animal! I suppose he's so tame because we've been kind to him."

"All mongooses are like that," said her husband. "If Teddy doesn't pick him up by the tail, or try to put him in a cage, he'll run in and out of the house all day long. Let's give him something to eat."

They gave him a little piece of raw meat. Rikki-tikki liked it greatly, and when it was finished, he went out into the veranda and sat in the sunshine and puffed up his fur to make it dry to the roots. Then he felt better.

"There are more things to find out about in this house," he said to himself, "than all my family could find out in all their lives. I shall certainly stay and find out."

He spent all that day looking around the house. He nearly drowned himself in the bathtubs, put his nose into the ink on a writing table, and burned it on the end of the big man's cigar, for he climbed up in the big man's lap to see how writing was done. At night he ran into Teddy's room to watch how kerosene lamps were lighted, and when Teddy went to bed Rikki-tikki climbed up too. But he was always moving. He had to get up and attend to every noise all through the night, and find out what made it. Teddy's mother and father came in, the last thing, to look at their boy. Rikki-tikki was awake on the pillow. "I don't like that," said Teddy's mother. "He may bite the child."

"He'll do no such thing," said the father. "Teddy's safer with that little beast than if he had a big hound to watch him. If a snake came into the room now—"

But Teddy's mother wouldn't think of anything so awful.

Early in the morning Rikki-tikki came to early breakfast in the veranda riding on Teddy's shoulder. They gave him banana and some boiled egg. He sat on all their laps one after the other, because every well-brought-up mongoose always hopes to be a house mongoose some day and have rooms to run about in.

Then Rikki-tikki went out into the garden to see what was to be seen. It was a large garden, only half plowed, with bushes, as big as small huts, of Marshal Niel roses, lime and orange trees, clumps of bamboos, and thickets of high grass. Rikki-tikki licked his lips. "This is a wonderful hunting ground," he said, and his tail grew bottle-brushy at the thought of it. He hurried up and down the garden,

snuffing here and there till he heard crying voices in a thornbush. It was Darzee the Tailorbird and his wife. They had made a beautiful nest by pulling two big leaves together and stitching them up the edges with fibers, and had filled the hollow with cotton and soft fluff. The nest moved from side to side as they sat on the rim and sobbed.

"What is the matter?" asked Rikki-tikki.

"We are very miserable," said Darzee. "One of our babies fell out of the nest yesterday and Nag ate him."

"H'm!" said Rikki-tikki, "that is very sad—but I am a stranger here. Who is Nag?"

Darzee and his wife only cowered down in the nest without answering, for from the thick grass at the foot of the bush there came a low hiss—a frightening cold sound that made Rikki-tikki jump back two clear feet. Then inch by inch out of the grass rose up the head and spread hood of Nag, the big black cobra. He was five feet long from tongue to tail. When he had lifted one-third of himself clear of the ground, he moved from side to side exactly as a dandelion grass balances in the wind. He looked at Rikki-tikki with the wicked snake's eyes that never change their stare, no matter what the snake may be thinking of.

"Who is Nag?" said he. *"I* am Nag. The great God

Brahm put his mark upon all our people, when the first cobra spread his hood to keep the sun off Brahm as he slept. Look, and be afraid!"

He spread out his hood more than ever. Rikki-tikki saw the mark on the back of it that looks exactly like the eye part of a hook-and-eye fastening. He was afraid for the minute, but it is impossible for a mongoose to stay frightened for any length of time. Though Rikki-tikki had never met a live cobra before, his mother had fed him on dead ones, and he knew that all a grown mongoose's business in life was to fight and eat snakes. Nag knew that, too, and at the bottom of his cold heart he was afraid.

"Well," said Rikki-tikki, and his tail began to puff up again, "marks or no marks, do you think it is right for you to eat young birds out of a nest?"

Nag was thinking to himself, and watching the least little movement in the grass behind Rikki-tikki. He knew that mongooses in the garden were signs of death sooner or later for him. He wanted to get Rikki-tikki off his guard. So he dropped his head a little, and put it on one side.

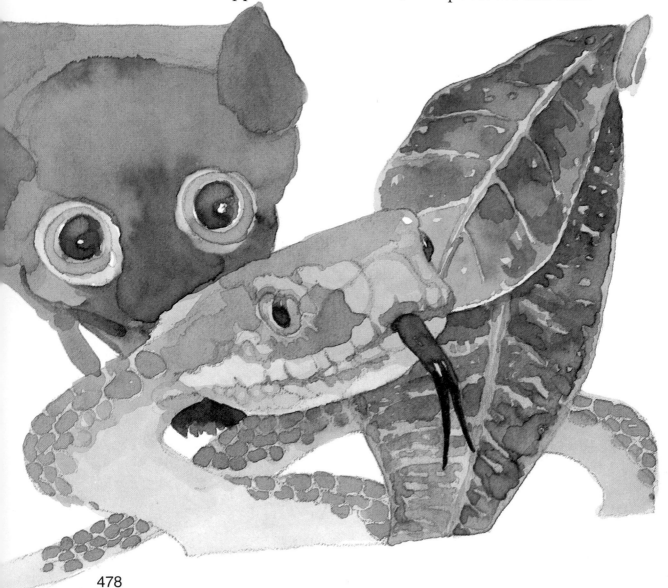

"Let us talk," he said. "You eat eggs. Why should not I eat birds?"

"Behind you! Look behind you!" sang Darzee.

Rikki-tikki knew better than to waste time in staring. He jumped up in the air as high as he could go, and just under him shot the head of Nagaina. She had crept up behind him as he was talking, to make an end of him. He heard her savage hiss as the stroke missed him. He came down almost across her back. If he had been an old mongoose he would have known that then was the time to break her back with one bite; but he was afraid of the terrible lashing return stroke of the snake. He bit, indeed, but he did not bite long enough, and he jumped clear of the whisking tail, leaving Nagaina torn and angry.

"Wicked, wicked Darzee!" said Nag, lashing up as high as he could reach toward the nest in the thornbush. But Darzee had built it out of reach of snakes, and it only moved with the wind.

Rikki-tikki felt his eyes growing red and hot (when a mongoose's eyes grow red, he is angry). He sat back on his tail and hind legs like a little kangaroo, and looked all round him, and chattered with rage. But Nag and Nagaina were gone, into the grass. When a snake misses its stroke, it never says anything or gives any sign of what it means to do next. Rikki-tikki did not care to follow them. He did not feel sure that he could handle two snakes at once. So he ran off to the rocky path near the house, and sat down to think. It was a serious matter for him.

If you read the old books of natural history, you will find they say that when the mongoose fights the snake and the snake bites, the mongoose runs off and eats a plant that cures him. That is not true. The victory is only a matter of how quick is the eye and the foot—snake's blow against mongoose's jump—and as no eye can follow the moves of a snake's head when it strikes, this makes things much more wonderful than any magic plant. Rikki-tikki knew he was a young mongoose, and it made him all the more pleased to think that he had escaped a blow from behind.

He felt good about the fight, and when Teddy came running down the path, Rikki-tikki was ready to be petted. But just as Teddy was stooping, something wiggled a little in the dust, and a tiny voice said: "Be careful. I am Death!"

It was Karait, the dusty brown snake that lies for choice on the dusty earth; and his bite is poison like the cobra's. But he is so small that nobody thinks of him, and so he does the more harm to people.

Rikki-tikki's eyes grew red again, and he danced up to Karait with the strange rocking, swaying motion that was known to his family. It looks very funny, but it is an exactly balanced move that you can fly off from at any angle you please, and in dealing with snakes this is an advantage.

If Rikki-tikki had only known, he was doing a much more dangerous thing than fighting Nag. For Karait is so small, and can turn so quickly, that unless Rikki bit him close to the back of the head, he would get the return stroke in his eye or his lip. But Rikki did not know. His eyes were all red, and he rocked back and forth, looking for a good place to hold. Karait attacked. Rikki jumped sideways and tried to run in, but the wicked little dusty gray head lashed next to his shoulder. He had to jump over the body, and the head followed his heels close.

Teddy shouted to the house: "Oh, look here! Our mongoose is killing a snake." And Rikki-tikki heard a scream from Teddy's mother. His father ran out with a stick, but by the time he came up, Karait had lunged out once too far. Rikki-tikki had sprung, jumped on the snake's back, dropped his head far between his forelegs, bitten as high up the back as he could get hold, and rolled away.

That bite stopped Karait, and Rikki-tikki was just going to eat him up from the tail, after the way of his family at dinner, when he remembered that a full meal makes a slow mongoose. If he wanted all his strength and quickness ready, he must keep himself thin. He went away for a dust bath under the castor-oil bushes, while Teddy's father beat the dead Karait.

"What is the use of that?" thought Rikki-tikki. "I have settled it all."

And then Teddy's mother picked him up from the dust

482

and hugged him, crying that he had saved Teddy from death. Teddy's father said that he was a providence, and Teddy looked on with big scared eyes. Rikki-tikki thought all the bother rather funny because, of course, he did not understand. Teddy's mother might just as well have petted Teddy for playing in the dust. Rikki was truly enjoying himself.

That night at dinner, walking among the glasses on the table, he might have stuffed himself three times over with nice things. But he remembered Nag and Nagaina. Though it was very pleasant to be patted and petted by Teddy's mother, and to sit on Teddy's shoulder, his eyes would get red from time to time, and he would go off into his long war cry of *"Rikk-tikk-tikki-tikki-tchk!"*

Teddy carried him off to bed, and insisted on Rikki-tikki sleeping under his chin. Rikki-tikki was too well bred to bite or scratch. As soon as Teddy was asleep he went off for his nightly walk round the house, and in the dark he ran up against Chuchundra the Muskrat creeping around by the wall. Chuchundra is a brokenhearted little beast. He whimpers and cheeps all the night, trying to make up his mind to run into the middle of the room. But he never gets there.

"Don't kill me," said Chuchundra, almost weeping. "Rikki-tikki, don't kill me!"

"Do you think a snake-killer kills muskrats?" said Rikki-tikki scornfully.

"Those who kill snakes get killed by snakes," said Chuchundra more sorrowfully than ever. "And how am I to be sure that Nag won't mistake me for you some dark night?"

"There's not the least danger," said Rikki-tikki. "But Nag is in the garden, and I know you don't go there."

"My cousin Chua the Rat told me—" said Chuchundra, and then he stopped.

"Told you what?"

"H'sh! Nag is everywhere, Rikki-tikki. You should have talked to Chua in the garden."

"I didn't—so you must tell me. Quick, Chuchundra, or I'll bite you!"

Chuchundra sat down and cried till the tears rolled off his whiskers. "I am a very poor man," he sobbed. "I never had spirit enough to run out into the middle of the room. H'sh! I mustn't tell you anything. Can't you *hear*, Rikki-tikki?"

Rikki-tikki listened. The house was as still as still, but he thought he could just catch the faintest *scratch-scratch* in the world—a noise as faint as that of a wasp walking on a windowpane—the dry scratch of a snake's scales on brickwork.

"That's Nag or Nagaina," he said to himself, "and he is crawling into the bathroom sluice. You're right, Chuchundra; I should have talked to Chua."

He stole off to Teddy's bathroom, but there was nothing there, and then to Teddy's mother's bathroom. At the bottom of the smooth plaster wall there was a brick pulled out to make a sluice for the bath water, and as Rikki-tikki stole in by the masonry curb where the bath is put, he heard Nag and Nagaina whispering together outside in the moonlight.

"When the house is emptied of people," said Nagaina, *"he* will have to go away, and then the garden will be our

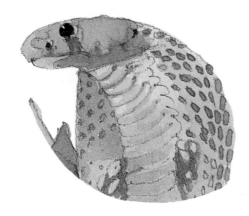

own again. Go in quietly, and remember that the big man who killed Karait is the first one to bite. Then come out and tell me, and we will hunt for Rikki-tikki together."

"But are you sure that there is anything to be gained by killing the people?" said Nag.

"Everything. When there were no people in the cottage, did we have any mongoose in the garden? So long as the cottage is empty, we are king and queen of the garden; and remember that as soon as my eggs in the melon bed hatch (as they may tomorrow), the children will need room and quiet."

"I had not thought of that," said Nag. "I will go, but there is no need that we should hunt for Rikki-tikki afterward. I will kill the big man and his wife, and the child if I can, and come away quietly. Then the cottage will be empty, and Rikki-tikki will go."

Rikki-tikki tingled all over with rage and hatred at this, and then Nag's head came through the sluice, and his five feet of cold body followed it. Angry as he was, Rikki-tikki was very frightened as he saw the size of the big cobra. Nag coiled himself up, raised his head, and looked into the bathroom in the dark, and Rikki could see his eyes glitter.

"Now, if I kill him here, Nagaina will know; and if I fight him on the open floor, the odds are in his favor. What am I to do?" said Rikki-tikki-tavi.

Nag waved back and forth, and then Rikki-tikki heard him drinking from the biggest water jar that was used to fill the bath. "That is good," said the snake. "Now, when Karait was killed, the big man had a stick. He may have that stick still, but when he comes in to bathe in the morning he will not have a stick. I shall wait here till he comes. Nagaina—do you hear me?—I shall wait here in the cool till daytime."

There was no answer from outside, so Rikki-tikki

knew Nagaina had gone away. Nag coiled himself down,
ring by ring, round the bulge at the bottom of the water
jar, and Rikki-tikki stayed still as death. After an hour he
began to move, muscle by muscle, toward the jar. Nag
was asleep, and Rikki-tikki looked at his big back, wondering which would be the best place for a good hold. "If I
don't break his back at the first jump," said Rikki, "he can
still fight. And if he fights—O Rikki!" He looked at the
thickness of the neck below the hood, but that was too
much for him; and a bite near the tail would only make
Nag savage.

"It must be the head," he said at last; "the head above

the hood. And, when I am once there, I must not let go."

Then he jumped. The head was lying a little clear of the water jug, under the curve of it; and, as his teeth met, Rikki braced his back against the bulge of the red earthenware to hold down the head. This gave him just one second's purchase, and he made the most of it. Then he was banged back and forth as a rat is shaken by a dog— back and forth on the floor, up and down, and around in great circles. His eyes were red and he held on as the body cartwhipped over the floor, upsetting the tin dipper and the soap dish and the flesh brush, and banged against the tin side of the bath.

As he held, he closed his jaws tighter and tighter. He was sure he would be banged to death, and, for the honor of his family, he wanted to be found with his teeth locked. He was dizzy, aching, and felt shaken to pieces when something went off like a clap of thunder just behind him. A hot wind knocked him senseless and red fire singed his fur. The big man had been wakened by the noise, and had fired both barrels of a shotgun into Nag just behind the hood.

Rikki-tikki held on with his eyes shut, for now he was quite sure he was dead. But the head did not move, and the big man picked him up and said, "It's the mongoose again, Alice. The little chap has saved *our* lives now."

Then Teddy's mother came in and saw what was left of Nag. Rikki-tikki dragged himself to Teddy's bedroom and spent half the rest of the night shaking himself tenderly to find out if he really was broken into forty pieces, as he fancied.

When morning came he was very stiff, but well pleased with his doings. "Now I have Nagaina to settle with, and she will be worse than five Nags. There's no knowing when the eggs she spoke of will hatch. Goodness! I must go and see Darzee," he said.

Without waiting for breakfast, Rikki-tikki ran to the thornbush where Darzee was singing a song of triumph

at the top of his voice. The news of Nag's death was all over the garden, for the sweeper had thrown the body on the rubbish heap.

"Oh, you stupid bunch of feathers!" said Rikki-tikki angrily. "Is this the time to sing?"

"Nag is dead—is dead—is dead!" sang Darzee. "The great Rikki-tikki caught him by the head and held fast. The big man brought the bang stick, and Nag fell in two pieces! He will never eat my babies again."

"All that's true enough. But where's Nagaina?" said Rikki-tikki, looking carefully round him.

"Nagaina came to the bathroom sluice and called for Nag," Darzee went on, "and Nag came out on the end of a stick—the sweeper picked him up on the end of a stick and threw him upon the rubbish pile. Let us sing about the great, the red-eyed Rikki-tikki!" And Darzee filled his throat and sang.

"If I could get up to your nest, I'd roll your babies out!" said Rikki-tikki. "You don't know when to do the right thing at the right time. You're safe enough in your nest there, but it's war for me down here. Stop singing a minute, Darzee."

"For the great, the beautiful Rikki-tikki's sake I will stop," said Darzee. "What is it, O Killer of the Terrible Nag?"

"Where is Nagaina, for the second time?"

"On the rubbish pile by the stables, mourning for Nag. Great is Rikki-tikki with the white teeth."

"Bother my white teeth! Have you ever heard where she keeps her eggs?"

"In the melon bed, on the end nearest the wall, where

the sun strikes nearly all day. She hid them there weeks ago."

"And you never thought it worth while to tell me? The end nearest the wall, you said?"

"Rikki-tikki, you are not going to eat her eggs?"

"Not eat exactly, no. Darzee, if you have a grain of sense you will fly off to the stables and pretend that your wing is broken, and let Nagaina chase you away to this bush. I must get to the melon bed. If I went there now she'd see me."

Darzee was a feather-brained little fellow who could never hold more than one idea at a time in his head. And just because he knew that Nagaina's children were born in eggs like his own, he didn't think at first that it was fair to kill them. But his wife was a sensible bird, and she knew that cobra's eggs meant young cobras later on. So she flew off from the nest, and left Darzee to keep the babies warm, and continue his song about the death of Nag.

She fluttered in front of Nagaina by the rubbish pile and cried out, "Oh, my wing is broken! The boy in the house threw a stone at me and broke it." Then she fluttered more desperately than ever.

Nagaina lifted up her head and hissed, "You warned Rikki-tikki when I would have killed him. Indeed and truly, you've chosen a bad place to be lame in." And Nagaina moved toward Darzee's wife, slipping along over the dust.

"The boy broke it with a stone!" shrieked the pretending bird.

"Well! It may be some consolation to you when you're dead to know that I shall settle accounts with the boy. Nag lies on the rubbish pile this morning, but before night the boy in the house will lie very still. What is the use of running away? I am sure to catch you. Little fool, look at me!"

Darzee's wife knew better than to do *that*, for any bird who looks at a snake's eyes gets so frightened that she cannot move. So she fluttered on, piping sorrowfully, and never leaving the ground, and Nagaina quickened her pace.

Rikki-tikki heard them going up the path from the stables, and he raced for the end of the melon patch near the wall. There, in the warm litter above the melons, very cunningly hidden, he found twenty-five eggs, about the size of a bantam's eggs, but with whitish skins instead of shells.

"I was not a day too soon," he said. He could see the baby snakes curled up inside the skin, and he knew that the minute they were hatched they could each kill a per-

son or a mongoose. He bit off the tops of the eggs as fast as he could, taking care to crush the young cobras, and turned over the litter from time to time to see if he had missed any. At last there were only three eggs left, and Rikki-tikki began to laugh to himself, when he heard the bird screaming:

"Rikki-tikki, I led Nagaina toward the house, and she has gone into the veranda, and—oh, come quickly—she means killing!"

Rikki-tikki destroyed two eggs, and tumbled backward down the melon bed with the third egg in his mouth, and hurried to the veranda as fast as he could put foot to the ground. Teddy and his mother and father were there at early breakfast. Rikki-tikki saw that they were not eating anything. They sat stone-still, and their faces were white. Nagaina was coiled up on the matting by Teddy's chair, within easy striking reach of Teddy's bare leg, and she was swinging from side to side, singing a song of triumph.

"Son of the big man that killed Nag," she hissed, "stay still. I am not ready yet. Wait a little. Keep very still, all you three! If you move I strike, and if you do not move I strike. Oh, foolish people, who killed Nag!"

Teddy's eyes were fixed on his father, and all his father could do was whisper, "Sit still, Teddy. You mustn't move. Teddy, keep still."

Then Rikki-tikki came up and cried, "Turn round, Nagaina. Turn and fight."

"All in good time," said she, without moving her eyes. "I will settle my account with *you* presently. Look at your friends, Rikki-tikki. They are still and white. They are

afraid. They dare not move, and if you come a step nearer
I strike."

"Look at your eggs," said Rikki-tikki, "in the melon
bed near the wall. Go and look, Nagaina!"

The big snake turned half around, and saw the egg on
the veranda. "Ah-h! Give it to me," she said.

Rikki-tikki put his paws one on each side of the egg,
and his eyes were blood-red. "What price for a snake's
egg? For a young cobra? For a young king cobra? For the
last—the very last of the brood? The ants are eating all the
others down by the melon bed."

Nagaina spun clear round, forgetting everything for the sake of the one egg. Rikki-tikki saw Teddy's father shoot out a big hand, catch Teddy by the shoulder, and drag him across the little table with the teacups, safe and out of reach of Nagaina.

"Tricked! Tricked! Tricked! *Rikk-tck-tck!*" chuckled Rikki-tikki. "The boy is safe, and it was—I—I—I that caught Nag by the hood last night in the bathroom." Then he began to jump up and down, all four feet together, his head close to the floor. "He threw me back and forth, but he could not shake me off. He was dead before the big man blew him in two. I did it! *Rikki-tikki-tck-tck!* Come then, Nagaina. Come and fight with me. You shall not be lonely long."

Nagaina saw that she had lost her chance of killing Teddy, and the egg lay between Rikki-tikki's paws. "Give me the egg, Rikki-tikki. Give me the last of my eggs, and I will go away and never come back," she said, lowering her hood.

"Yes, you will go away, and you will never come back. For you will go to the rubbish pile with Nag. Fight! The big man has gone for his gun! Fight!"

Rikki-tikki was bounding all round Nagaina, keeping just out of reach of her stroke, his little eyes like hot coals. Nagaina gathered herself together and flung out at him. Rikki-tikki jumped up and backward. Again and again and again she struck. Each time her head came with a smack on the matting of the veranda and she gathered herself together like a watch spring. Then Rikki-tikki danced in a circle to get behind her. Nagaina turned around to keep her head to his head, so that the rubbing

of her tail on the matting sounded like dry leaves blown along by the wind.

He had forgotten the egg. It still lay on the veranda, and Nagaina came nearer and nearer to it, till at last, while Rikki-tikki was drawing breath, she caught it in her mouth, turned to the veranda steps, and shot like an arrow down the path, with Rikki-tikki behind her. When the cobra runs for her life, she goes like a whip flashing across a horse's neck. Rikki-tikki knew that he must catch her, or all the trouble would begin again.

She headed straight for the long grass by the thorn-bush, and as he was running Rikki-tikki heard Darzee still singing his foolish little song of triumph. But Darzee's wife was wiser. She was off her nest as Nagaina came along, and flapped her wings about Nagaina's head. If Darzee had helped they might have turned her, but Nagaina only lowered her hood and went on. Still, that helpful instant brought Rikki-tikki up to her, and as she dived into the rat hole where she used to live, his little white teeth were clenched on her tail. He went down with her—and very few mongooses, however wise and old they may be, care to follow a cobra into its hole.

It was dark in the hole; and Rikki-tikki never knew when it might open out and give Nagaina room to turn and attack him. He held on savagely, and stuck out his feet to act as brakes on the dark bank of the hot, damp earth.

Then the grass by the mouth of the hole stopped waving, and Darzee said, "It is all over with Rikki-tikki! We must sing his death song. Great Rikki-tikki is dead! For Nagaina will surely kill him underground."

So he sang a very mournful song that he made up on the spur of the minute. Just as he got to the most touching part, the grass quivered again, and Rikki-tikki, covered with dirt, dragged himself out of the hole leg by leg, licking his whiskers. Darzee stopped with a little shout. Rikki-tikki shook some of the dust out of his fur and sneezed. "It is all over," he said. "Nagaina will never come out again." And the red ants that live between the grass stems heard him, and began to troop down one after another to see if he had spoken the truth.

Rikki-tikki curled himself up in the grass and slept where he was—slept and slept till it was late in the afternoon, for he had done a hard day's work.

"Now," he said, when he awoke, "I will go back to the

house. Tell the Coppersmith, Darzee, and he will tell the garden that Nagaina is dead.''

The Coppersmith is a bird who makes a noise exactly like the beating of a little hammer on a copper pot. The reason he is always making it is because he is the town crier to every Indian garden. He tells all the news to

499

everybody who cares to listen. As Rikki-tikki went up the path, he heard the Coppersmith's "attention" notes like a tiny dinner gong, and then the steady *"Ding-dong-tock! Nag is dead—dong! Nagaina is dead! Ding-dong-tock!"* That set all the birds in the garden singing, and the frogs croaking, for Nag and Nagaina used to eat frogs as well as little birds.

When Rikki got to the house, Teddy and Teddy's mother and Teddy's father came out and almost cried over him; and that night he ate all that was given him till he could eat no more, and went to bed on Teddy's shoulder, where Teddy's mother saw him when she came to look late at night.

"He saved our lives and Teddy's life," she said to her husband. "Just think, he saved all our lives."

Rikki-tikki woke up with a jump, for the mongooses are light sleepers.

"Oh, it's you," said he. "What are you bothering for? All the cobras are dead. And if they weren't, I'm here."

Rikki-tikki had a right to be proud of himself. But he did not grow too proud, and he kept that garden as a mongoose should keep it, with tooth and jump and spring and bite, till never a cobra dared show its head inside the walls.

About the Author

Rudyard Kipling was born in India in 1865. His parents were from England. The love he felt for India is shown in many of his stories. He won the Nobel Prize for literature in 1907.

Glossary

Entries adapted from *The HBJ School Dictionary,* copyright © 1977, 1972, 1968 by Harcourt Brace Jovanovich, Inc., are reprinted by permission of the publisher.

Key to Pronunciation
Listed below are diacritical symbols and key words. The boldface letters in the key words represent the sounds indicated by the symbols.

/ā/	cake	/d/	duck
/a/	hat	/ē/	bean
/ä/	father	/e/	pet
/är/	car	/f/	fun
/âr/	care	/g/	go
/b/	boy	/gz/	exact
/ch/	church	/h/	home

/(h)w/	white	/ou/	out
/ī/	pie	/p/	pet
/i/	pig	/r/	run
/ir/	dear	/s/	see
/j/	jump	/sh/	ship
/k/	kite	/t/	top
/ks/	box	/th/	thin
/kw/	quit	/th/	this
/l/	look	/u/	nut
/m/	man	/ûr/	fur
/n/	not	/v/	vine
/ng/	sing	/w/	will
/ō/	rope	/y/	yes
/o/	top	/yo͞o/	use
/ô/	saw	/z/	zoo
/oi/	oil	/zh/	azure
/o͞o/	moon	/ə/	above
/o͝o/	book		circus
/ôr/	fork	/ər/	bitter

Aa

ab·jure [ab·jo͞or′] *v.* **ab·jured** To take an oath publicly to give up something: He *abjured* his outdated theory.

a·brupt [ə·brupt′] *adj.* 1. Sudden: We made an *abrupt* turn in order to miss the uprooted tree. 2. Rude or curt, as in speech; brusque.—**a·brupt′ly** *adv.*

ac·cel·er·a·tion [ak·sel′ə·rā′shən] *n.* An increase in speed or velocity.

ac·com·plish [ə·kom′plish] *v.* **ac·com·plish·ing** 1. To carry out; effect: Ruth was *accomplishing* through hard work what we thought was impossible. 2. To finish.

ac·cus·tomed [ə·kus′təmd] *adj.* Habitual; usual.—**accustomed to** In the habit of; used to.

a·cryl·ic [ə·kril′ik] *n.* A kind of paint with a thermoplastic base.

a·dapt [ə·dapt′] *v.* To adjust to new conditions: The polar bear has *adapted* itself to the Arctic.

ad·van·tage [ad·van′tij] *n.* Any circumstance or condition that benefits someone or helps toward success.

aisle [īl] *n.* A passageway, as in a theater or church, that separates one section of seats from another section.

al·ly [al′ī] *n., pl.* **al·lies** A person or country joined with another for a particular purpose: The United States and England were *allies* during World War II.

a·maze [ə·māz′] *v.* **a·mazed, a·maz·ing** To bewilder with wonder or surprise; astonish, perplex: His knowledge *amazed* his teachers.

a·maze·ment [ə·māz′mənt] *n.* Bewilderment resulting from surprise; astonishment: Her *amazement* increased with each successive jump of the high wire act.

am·bas·sa·dor [am·bas′ə·dər] *n.* An official of the highest rank sent to represent a government in another country.

an·chor [ang′kər] *n.* A metal object with hooks that grip the bottom, lowered into the water by a chain or rope to keep a ship from drifting.

an·gle·worm [ang′gəl·wûrm′] *n.* An earthworm.

an·nounce·ment [ə·nouns′mənt] *n.* An often formal public or private notice of an event: a wedding *announcement*.

an·noy [ə·noi′] *v.* **an·noyed** To bother; irritate: His loud talking *annoyed* me.

ap·pe·tiz·ing [ap′ə·tī′zing] *adj.* Stimulating a desire for food.

ap·point·ment [ə·point′mənt] *n.* An agreement to meet someone at a certain place and time.

apt [apt] *adj.* Having a natural tendency; likely.

arch [ärch] *n.* A curved structure over an opening, capable of holding up material above it.

ar·chi·tect [är′kə·tekt] *n.* A person who designs and draws up plans for buildings or other structures.

a·ri·a [ä′rē·ə] *n.* A song, usually in an opera or oratorio, sung by a single person to musical accompaniment.

a·shamed [ə·shāmd′] *adj.* Feeling upset because something bad, silly, or improper was done.

as·par·a·gus [ə·spar′ə·gəs] *n.*
1. A perennial plant related to the lily.
2. Its young shoots, eaten as a vegetable.

as·sem·bly [ə·sem′blē] *n.* A gathering or meeting together of persons.

as·tro·naut [as′trə·nôt] *n.* A person who travels in space.

at·mos·phere [at′məs·fir] *n.* The air surrounding the earth.

au·to·graph [ô′tə·graf] 1. *n.* A person's name written in his or her own handwriting. 2. *v.* To write one's name on: The movie stars *autographed* their pictures.

av·er·age [av′rij] *n.* The sum of the elements in a set of numbers divided by the number of elements in the set: The *average* of 4, 6, and 5 is 5.

a·wak·en [ə·wā′kən] *v.* **a·wak·ened** To stop sleeping; wake up.

awe [ô] *v.* **awed** To make feel fear and wonder at the size, power, majesty, etc., of something: We were *awed* by

the violence of the tropical thunderstorm.

az·ure [azh′ər] *adj.* Sky blue.

Bb

bab·ble [bab′əl] *n.* Foolish or fast talk.

bal·ance [bal′əns] *n.* The ability to keep one's body in a desired position without falling.

bam·boo [bam·bōō′] *n.* A tall, tropical grass with hollow, jointed stems that are used in building and in making furniture, utensils, poles, etc.

band·saw [band·sô] *n.* A power cutting tool consisting of an endless toothed steel belt.

bank [bangk] *n., pl.* **banks** The land along the edge of a river or stream: The south *bank* of the Red River marks much of the boundary between Texas and Oklahoma.

ban·quet [bang′kwit] *n.* A lavish feast.

ban·tam [ban′təm] *n.* A breed of small chickens, known for their fighting ability.

bar·gain [bär′gən] *n.* 1. An agreement between people about something to be done or traded. 2. Something bought or offered for sale at less than its usual price. —**into the bargain** In addition; besides: The dog's lazy, and stupid *into the bargain.*

barge [bärj] 1. *n.* A large, flat-bottomed boat used to carry freight in harbors, rivers, and other inland waters. 2. *v. informal* To enter or intrude quickly and rudely.

ba·ton [bə·ton′] *n.* A slender stick or rod used by a conductor in leading an orchestra.

bat·ting cage [bat′ing kāj] *n.* A box-like structure, closed on all but one side by wire mesh, used for batting practice.

bawl [bôl] *v.* **bawled** 1. To cry or sob noisily: The baby *bawled* until it was fed. 2. To call out loudly and harshly; shout; bellow.

be·head [bi·hed′] *v.* To cut off the head of.

be·wil·der [bi·wil′dər] *v.* **be·wil·dered** To puzzle and confuse; baffle: Every-one was *bewildered* by the horse's strange behavior.

bid·ding [bid′ing] *n.* Command; order.

bind [bīnd] *v.* To tie or fasten, as with a band or cord.

bit·tern [bit′ərn] *n.* A long-legged bird that lives in swamps and marshes and has a harsh cry.

bleat [blēt] *v.* **bleat·ing** To utter the cry of a sheep, goat, or calf.

bliz·zard [bliz′ərd] *n.* A heavy snow-storm accompanied by strong, freezing wind.

blos·som [blos′əm] *n.* A flower.

blush [blush] *v.* **blushed** To become red in the face, as from embarrassment or confusion: Jan *blushed* when she accidentally walked into the wall.

boast [bōst] *v.* **boast·ed** To talk in a vain or bragging manner: The fisherman *boasted* about the day's catch of fish.

bo·lo tie [bō′lō tī] *n.* A kind of necktie fastened with an ornamental clasp: The *bolo tie* was made of black cord and had a metal clasp.

bon·fire [bon′fīr′] *n.* A fire built outdoors.

booth [bōōth] *n.* A place where goods are displayed or sold at an exhibition or fair.

bra·vo [brä′vō] *interj.* Well done: The audience yelled *"bravo"* at the end of the performance.

bril·liant [bril′yənt] *adj.* Sparkling or glowing with light; very bright.

broad [brôd] *adj.* Large in width; wide.

brood [brōōd] *n.* All of the young of the same mother.

brow [brou] *n.* 1. The front, upper part of the head; forehead. 2. The eyebrow. 3. The upper edge of a steep place: the *brow* of a hill.

bub·bler [bub′(ə)lər] *n.* A drinking fountain from which water bubbles upwards.

buck [buk] *n.* The male of certain animals, as of antelope, deer, rabbits, goats, etc.

butte [byōōt] *n.* A hill, standing alone, that has steep sides and sometimes a flat top.

Cc

ca·nal [kə·nal′] *n.* A waterway that is built across land and used by ships or boats or for supplying water to dry areas.

ca·noe [kə·nōō′] *n.* A small, light boat, pointed at both ends and moved by paddles.

can·ton·ment [kan·ton′mənt] *n.* A station for the temporary housing of troops.

cap·tiv·i·ty [kap·tiv′ə·tē] *n.* The condition of being held captive; confinement; imprisonment.

care·less [kâr′lis] *adj.* Not giving close attention to what one is doing or saying: Su was *careless* and left her book at a friend's house.—**care′less·ly** *adv.*

cas·u·al [kazh′ōō·əl] *adj.* Happening by chance; unexpected: a *casual* meeting.—**cas′u·al·ly** *adv.*

cat·nap [kat′nap] *n.* A time of sleep, especially a short period of sleep during the day.

cat·nip [kat′nip] *n.* A fragrant herb of the mint family.

cav·al·ry [kav′əl·rē] *n.* In the past, soldiers who were trained to fight on horseback.

cav·i·ty [kav′ə·tē] *n., pl.* **cav·i·ties** A hollow place in a tooth caused by decay.

cel·lo [chel′ō] *n.* A large instrument like a violin but bigger, with a deep tone: The *cello* is held between the performer's knees when played.

cham·ber [chām′bər] *n.* A hollow or enclosed space.

check [chek] *v.* 1. To deposit or put in temporary safekeeping. 2. To test or examine for accuracy, completeness, etc.: to *check* a column of addition.

chick·a·dee [chik′ə·dē] *n.* A small bird having the top of its head and its throat of a darker color than the body.

chis·el [chiz′(ə)l] *n.* A cutting tool with a sharp, beveled edge, used to cut or shape wood, metal, or stone.

cho·rus [kôr′əs] *n.* A group of singers, speakers, or dancers that perform together.

cin·der [sin′dər] *n.* 1. A piece of partly burned wood, coal, etc., that is not flaming. 2. *pl.* Charred bits and ashes from a fire: Always see that the *cinders* are scattered and cool before leaving a campsite.

cir·cum·stance [sûr′kəm·stans] *n.* An event, fact, or detail: The *circumstances* of the crime were not clear, so no one was arrested.

cit·y coun·cil [sit′ē koun′səl] *n.* An elected body responsible for city or town policy.

cit·y man·ag·er [sit′ē man′ij·ər] *n.* A person appointed by a city government to take charge of its operations.

civ·il [siv′əl] *adj.* 1. Of or having to do with citizens or citizenship. 2. Courteous; polite.

claim [klām] *n.* Something that is considered property, as a piece of land.

clar·i·net [klar′ə·net] *n.* A high-pitched woodwind musical instrument having a cylindrical body and a single-reed mouthpiece.

clasp [klasp] *v.* To grasp or embrace.

clench [klench] *v.* **clenched** To grasp or grip firmly: Elizabeth *clenched* the rail tightly as she looked over the edge of the cliff.

clev·er [klev′ər] *adj.* Good at learning or solving problems; bright; ingenious.

cliff [klif] *n.* A high, steep face of rock rising sharply above the ground or water below.

clip·board [klip′bôrd′] *n.* A board with a clasp at the top, used to hold papers for writing.

co·bra [kō′brə] *n.* A very poisonous snake of Asia and Africa that can swell its neck into a hood when excited.

505

cock·er span·iel
[kok′ər span′yəl]
n. A small dog
with long ears and
silky hair, used as
a house pet and for
hunting.

co·co·nut [kō′kə·nut′] *n.* The large
fruit of the coconut palm with a hard
shell, white meat, and a center filled
with a sweet liquid.

col·lapse [kə·laps′] *v.* **col·lapsed** To
lose health or strength: He *collapsed*
from overwork.

colo·nel [kûr′nəl] *n.* A military rank:
In the U.S. Army, a *colonel* is a com-
missioned officer ranking below a
brigadier general.

com·man·der [kə·man′dər] *n.* A person
who directs a ship, military force, etc.

com·mence [kə·mens′] *v.* **com·menced**
To start; initiate; begin: The construc-
tion *commenced* the first week in
May.

com·mis·sion [kə·mish′ən] *n.* An official body chosen to govern in some
cities.

com·mo·tion [kə·mō′shən] *n.* Great
confusion; excitement; disturbance.

com·pass [kum′pəs] *n.* An instrument
that shows direction, usually by a
magnetic needle that always points to
magnetic north.

com·put·er [kəm·pyōō′tər] *n.* An electronic device capable of doing arithmetic with great speed and accuracy.

con·cen·trate [kon′sən·trāt] *v.* **con·
cen·trat·ed** To gather or collect closely
together: The main part of the city

was *concentrated* in the downtown
area.

con·dense [kən·dəns′] *v.* To make or
become denser, thicker, or more com-
pressed, as by removing water.

con·duc·tor [kən·duk′tər] *n.* A person
who leads or guides.

con·fu·sion [kən·fyōō′zhən] *n.* 1. A
mixed-up or disordered state of mind
or of things. 2. Commotion; turmoil.

con·grat·u·late [kən·grach′ōō·lāt] *v.*
con·grat·u·lat·ed To express one's pleasure at the success or good fortune of:
We *congratulated* her on her
promotion.

con·grat·u·la·tion [kən·grach′ōō·
lā′shən] *n., pl.* **con·grat·u·la·tions**
1. The act of expressing good wishes.
2. Good wishes: It was nice to offer
congratulations.

con·so·la·tion [kon′sə·lā′shən] *n.* The
act of comforting (someone) in sorrow
or disappointment.

con·stit·u·ent [kən·stich′ōō·ənt]
1. *adj.* Necessary in making up a whole.
2. *n.* A voter represented by an elected
official: The senator asked his
constituents for their opinions.

con·tent·ment [kən·tent′mənt] *n.* Calm
satisfaction; peaceful happiness.

con·ven·ient [kən·vēn′yənt] *adj.* Suited
to one's purpose, plans, or comfort.

Corps of En·gi·neers [kôr uv en′jə·
nirz′] *n.* A special branch of the army
that not only builds for the army, but
also builds such things as dams,
lakes, and canals.

cos·tume [kos′t(y)ōōm] *n.* The clothing, ornaments, and arrangement of

hair worn by an actor or masquerader.

cove [kōv] *n.* A small, sheltered bay or inlet in a shoreline.

cow·er [kou′ər] *v.* To crouch, as in fear or shame; tremble: A frightened rabbit *cowered* under a bush.

coy·o·te [kī·ō′tē] A small wolf of the western prairies of North America.

cro·cus [krō′kəs] *n.* A small plant having cup-shaped yellow, purple, or white flowers.

cro·quet [krō·kā′] *n.* An outdoor game in which the players use mallets with long handles to drive wooden balls through a series of wire arches.

cur·rant [kûr′ənt] *n.* 1. A small, sour, red, white, or black berry. 2. A small seedless raisin used in cooking.

curt·sy [kûrt′sē] *v.* **curt·sy·ing** To make a bow: The young girls were *curtsying* with grace and poise.

Dd

dawn [dôn] *n.* The first appearance of light in the morning.

daz·zle [daz′(ə)l] *v.* **daz·zling** To blind or dim the vision of by too much light: The flood lights were *dazzling* the onlookers.

de·lib·er·ate [*adj.* di·lib′ər·it, *v.* di·lib′ə· rāt] 1. *adj.* Thought about and in-

tended. 2. *v.* To consider carefully; ponder.—**de·lib′er·ate·ly** *adv.*

del·i·cate [del′ə·kit] *adj.* Weak or easily injured.

de·light [di·līt′] *v.* To please extremely: Lillian was *delighted* at hearing the good news.

den·i·zen [den′ə·zən] *n.* A person, plant, or animal that lives or is found in a particular place.

de·pot [dē′pō] *n.* A railroad station.

de·pres·sion [di·presh′ən] *n.* A time when business is sharply cut down and many people are out of work.

de·scend [di·send′] *v.* To come or derive by birth from a certain source: He is *descended* from a duke.

de·sert [di·zûrt′] *v.* To leave a person, place, or thing; abandon: to *desert* one's home.—**de·sert′ed** *adj.*

des·per·ate [des′pər·it] *adj.* Reckless because all hope or choice seems gone.—**des′per·ate·ly** *adv.*

des·ti·na·tion [des′tə·nā′shən] *n.* The place toward which someone or something is traveling; goal: Their *destination* is Chicago.

dike [dīk] *n.* A dam or wall to keep back a river or sea from low land.

dim [dim] *adj.* Lacking enough light; not bright.—**dim′ly** *adv.*

dis·gust [dis·gust′] *n.* Strong dislike caused by something offensive.

dis·miss [dis·mis′] *v.* To tell or permit to leave.

dodge [doj] *v.* **dodged** To move aside suddenly: The player *dodged* and fell back to his right.

doe [dō] *n.* The female of the deer, antelope, rabbit, and certain other animals.

down·hill [doun'hil'] *adv.* Toward a lower elevation.

drift·wood [drift'wŏŏd'] *n.* Weathered timber or lumber carried by the water or washed up on the shore.

drill [dril] *n.* 1. A kind of instruction based on the repetition of physical or mental exercises. 2. Such an exercise, aimed at perfecting a skill or kind of knowledge: piano *drills.*

du·et [d(y)ŏŏ·et'] *n.* A piece of music to be played or sung by two performers.

dug·out [dug'out'] *n.* A low, covered shelter at a baseball diamond, in which players sit when not on the field.

dull [dul] 1. *adj.* Not bright or clear: *dull* colors; a *dull* sound. 2. *v.* To make or become dull: to *dull* the appetite: The old man's eyesight *dulled.*

du·pli·cate [d(y)ŏŏ'plə·kāt] *v.* To copy exactly or do again.

Ee

eel [ēl] *n.* A fish with a long, thin, snakelike body.

e·lect [i·lekt'] **e·lect·ed** *v.* To choose for an office by vote; select: to *elect* a mayor.

el·lipse [i·lips'] *n.* A closed curve which is a set of points so located that the sum of the distances from any point to two interior points, called the foci, is constant: Halley's Comet travels in an *ellipse* around the sun.

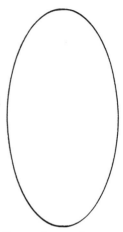

e·mer·gen·cy [i·mûr'jən·sē] *n., pl.* **e·mer·gen·cies** A sudden and unexpected turn of events calling for immediate action: The police officers helped at two *emergencies* this afternoon.

en·close [in·klōz'] *v.* **en·closed** To close in on all sides; surround.

es·sen·tial [ə·sen'shəl] *adj.* Extremely important or necessary; vital.

ev·i·dence [ev'ə·dəns] *n.* Something that proves what is true or not true.

ex·as·per·ate [ig·zas'pə·rāt] *v.* **ex·as·per·at·ed** To annoy or irritate almost to the point of anger: His constant lateness *exasperated* her.

ex·e·cute [ek'sə·kyŏŏt] *v.* **ex·e·cut·ed** 1. To follow or carry out; do. 2. To put to death by legal order.

ex·haus·tion [ig·zôs'chən] *n.* Extreme weariness or fatigue.

ex·per·i·ment [ik·sper'ə·mənt] *n.* Any test or trial that one makes in order to gain knowledge.

ex·plore [ik·splôr'] *v.* To travel in or through in order to learn or discover something.

ex·traor·di·nar·y [ik·strôr′də·ner′ē *or* eks′trə·ôr′də·ner′ē] *adj.* Remarkable; unusual; surprising.

ex·treme [ik·strēm′] *adj.* Very great or severe.

eye·tooth [ī′tooth] *n., pl.* **eye·teeth** [ī′tēth′] One of two upper teeth near the front of the mouth. It is the third tooth from the middle on either side.

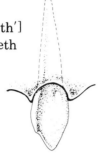

Ff

fal·con [fal′kən *or* fô(l)′kən] *n.* A swift hawk trained to hunt other birds and small animals.

fang [fang] *n.* A long, hollow, or grooved tooth with which a poisonous snake injects its poison.

fau·cet [fô′sit] *n.* A device with an adjustable valve used to start, stop, or regulate the flow of a liquid, as from a pipe; spigot.

fawn [fôn] *n.* A young deer not yet a year old.

fern [fûrn] *n.* Any of a large class of plants with featherlike leaves that have no flowers or seeds.

fer·til·iz·er [fûr′təl·ī′zər] *n.* A substance, such as manure or certain chemicals, applied to soil to furnish food for plants.

fetch [fech] *v.* **fetched** To go for, get, and bring back: The dog *fetched* the stick that she threw into the water.

fierce [fîrs] *adj.* Frighteningly savage, cruel, violent, or intense: The swamp deer ran from the *fierce* tiger.— **fierce·ly** *adv.*

filth·y [fil′thē] *adv.* Dirty; covered with filth.

fink [fink] *n., slang* A person regarded as obnoxious.

first-aid kit [fûrst·ād kit] *n.* A small package of supplies, such as medicines and bandages, that are used in medical emergencies.

fleet [flēt] *adj.* Rapid in movement; swift.

flick [flik] *v.* **flick·ing** To move with a light, snapping movement: The cat lay in the yard *flicking* its tail back and forth.

flip·per [flip′ər] *n.* A broad, flat shoe like a fin, worn by skin divers.

flock [flok] 1. *n.* A group of animals of the same kind herded, feeding, or moving together. 2. *v.* To come or move together in a crowd.

flus·ter [flus′tər] *v.* To make confused or upset.

foot·bridge [foot′brij′] *n.* A structure across a stream or canyon for people who are walking.

for·mer [fôr′mər] *adj.* Belonging to the past; previous; earlier.

for·tune tel·ler [fôr′chən tel′ər] *n.* A person claiming to foretell the future—**fortune-telling** *n., adj.*

frail [frā(ə)l] *adj.* Easily damaged in body or structure; weak.

fraz·zle [fraz′(ə)l] *v.* 1. To make or become ragged; fray. 2. To tire out; exhaust.—**fraz′ zled** *adj.*

frus·trate [frus′trāt] *v.* To baffle the efforts of or bring to nothing; foil.—**frus′trat·ed** *adj.*

fu·ry [fyoͦr′ē] *n.* 1. Wild or extreme anger; rage. 2. Great force or violence.

Gg

ga·la [gā′lə] *n.* A lively celebration; festival.

gal·lop [gal′əp] *n., v.* **gal·lop·ing** 1. The fastest gait of a four-footed animal: Nan had the horse run in a *gallop.* 2. *v.* To go at a fast pace.

gan·der [gan′dər] *n.* A male goose.

gas [gas] *n., pl.* **gas·es** A substance that is not solid or liquid but is fluid and able to expand indefinitely: Oxygen and hydrogen are *gases* at normal temperatures.

gasp [gasp] *v.* **gasp·ing** To suddenly catch one's breath: She was *gasping* for breath after the run.

gen·ius [jēn′yəs] *n.* A person who possesses an extremely high degree of mental power or talent.

ge·og·ra·phy [jē·og′rə·fē] *n.* The study of the features of a planet's surface.

gey·ser [gī′zər] *n.* A natural spring which at intervals sends up a fountain of water, steam, or mud.

gill [gil] *n.* The organ for breathing of fishes and other animals that live underwater.

glam·or·ous [glam′ər·əs] *adj.* Full of charm, beauty, or fascination.

gleam [glēm] 1. *n.* The shine of reflected light upon a surface. 2. *v.* To shine with a gleam.

glimpse [glimps] 1. *n.* A momentary view or look. 2. *v.* To see for a moment.

goods [goͦodz] *n., pl.* Anything made to be sold; merchandise.

gov·ern·ment [guv′ər(n)·mənt] *n.* System of the administration of the affairs of a nation, state, city, etc.

grate [grāt] *v.* To rub together so as to make a scraping sound: The bent fender *grated* on the wheel.

grave [grāv] *adj.* Of great importance; weighty: We were saddened by his *grave* words.—**grave′ly** *adv.*

grav·el [grav′əl] *n.* A mixture of small, rounded pebbles and pieces of stone.

grav·i·ty [grav′ə·tē] *n.* The force by which the earth, the moon, or a planet attracts objects on or near its surface, as shown by the tendency of objects to fall toward the center of the earth.

grouse [grous] *n.* A plump bird, often hunted for sport.

Gua·da·lu·pe Moun·tains [gwod·loo′pē] *n.* A range in southern New Mexico and western Texas.

gua·no [gwä′nō] *n.* The manure of sea birds or bats, used as fertilizer.

guin·ea pig [gin′ē pig] *n.* A small, ratlike animal with a short tail.

gulp [gulp] *v.* To drink in large swallows: Because he was late, Harry *gulped* down the glass of milk and rushed out the door.

Hh

hast·y [hās′tē] *adj.* Quick.—**hast′i·ly** *adv.*

hearth [härth] *n.* The fireside; home.

heath·er [heth′ər] *n.* A low evergreen shrub related to heath, having small pinkish flowers.

herd [hûrd] 1. *n.* A large group of animals of one kind, moving about or kept together in a group. 2. *v.* To gather or form into a herd.

his·to·ry [his′tə·rē] *n.* Past events, or a record of them, often concerning a particular nation, people, or activity.

hol·ler [hol′ər] *v., informal* **hol·ler·ing** To shout: They were *hollering* to us as we followed them up the trail.

hol·low [hol′ō] *adj.* Empty on the inside; not solid.

hoop skirt [hoop skûrt] *n.* A skirt puffed out with hoops.

hope·less [hōp′lis] *adj.* Without hope.

hor·i·zon [hə·rī′zən] *n.* The line where the earth and sky seem to meet.

hor·ri·fy [hôr′ə·fī] *v.* To fill with fear or loathing: The sight of a monster walking across the moor would *horrify* anyone.—**hor′ri·fied** *adj.*

hud·dle [hud′(ə)l] *v.* **hud·dled** To crowd or nestle together closely: The puppies *huddled* together for warmth.

hul·la·ba·loo [hul′ə·bə·loo′] *n.* An uproar; tumult.

hum·ming·bird [hum′ing·bûrd′] *n.* A tiny, brightly colored bird with a long bill. It moves its wings so rapidly that they hum.

hu·mor [(h)yoo′mər] *n.* The quality of being funny or amusing.

hunch [hunch] *v.* To bend or draw, as into a hump.

hy·a·cinth [hī′ə·sinth] *n.* A plant related to the lily, having a spikelike cluster of fragrant bell-shaped flowers.

Ii

im·pos·si·ble [im·pos′ə·bəl] *adj.* Not capable of being, being done, or taking place; not possible.

in·ca·pa·ble [in·kā′pə·bəl] *adj.* Lacking the necessary ability, skill, or capacity.

in·cred·i·ble [in·kred′ə·bəl] *adj.* So strange, unusual, or extraordinary as to be unbelievable.

in·dig·nant [in·dig′nənt] *adj.* Angry because of something that is not right, just, fair, etc. —**in·dig′nant·ly** *adv.*

in·gre·di·ent [in·grē′dē·ənt] *n.* Something put into a mixture as a part of it.

in·ning [in′ing] *n.* A part of a baseball game during which each team has a turn at bat until it makes three outs.

in·no·cent [in′ə·sənt] *adj.* Free from sin, blame, or evil; guiltless.—**in′no·cent·ly** *adv.*

in·sist [in·sist′] *v.* **in·sist·ed** To demand with determination: I *insisted* that he finish it.

in·spi·ra·tion [in′spə·rā′shən] *n.* 1. A good idea or impulse that comes to someone, usually suddenly. 2. A person or thing that arouses a feeling or idea in someone.

in·stru·ment [in′strə·mənt] *n.* A device for producing musical sounds, as a piano or trumpet.

in·ward [in′wərd] *adv.* Toward the inside.

ir·ri·tate [ir′ə·tāt] *v.* 1. To annoy; bother: The noise *irritated* her. 2. To make sore or inflamed.

i·so·late [ī′sə·lāt] *v.* **i·so·lat·ed** To place apart or alone; separate from others: His unfriendliness *isolated* him from the team.

Jj

ju·ry [joॖor′ē] *n.* A qualified group of people sworn to give a true verdict after hearing the evidence in a trial in a court of law.

Kk

ker·o·sene [ker′ə·sēn] *n.* A thin oil made from petroleum, used as fuel in lamps, stoves, etc.

kil·o·me·ter [kil′ə·mē′tər *or* ki·lom′ə·tər] *n.* In the metric system, 1,000 meters, a unit of length equal to about 5/8 of a mile.

kin·dling [kind′ling] *n.* Small pieces of dry wood for starting a fire.

Ll

la·ma [lä′mə] *n.* A Buddhist priest or monk in Tibet or Mongolia.

lame [lām] *adj.* Crippled or disabled, especially in a leg or foot.

lash [lash] *v.* **lash·ing** To move back and forth in a whiplike manner: The dog was *lashing* its tail in excitement.

lass [las] *n.* A young woman; girl.

launch [lônch] *v.* To hurl; fling.

laze [lāz] *v.* **laz·ing** To be unwilling to work or to keep busy; to be indolent: Instead of swimming, we spent our time *lazing* around the edge of the pool.

lean-to [lēn′tōō′] *n.* A rough shelter, sloping to the ground at one end.

lime·stone [līm′stōn′] *n.* A type of rock, as marble, that contains mainly calcium carbonate.

limp [limp] *adj.* Lacking stiffness; flabby.

loom [lōōm] *n.* A machine on which thread or yarn is woven into cloth.

lum·ber·jack [lum′bər·jak] *n.* A person whose work it is to saw down trees and transport them to the sawmill.

lunge [lunj] *v.* **lunged** To make a quick movement or plunge forward: Chris *lunged* for the bus just as its door closed and it moved away from the curb.

lure [lōōr] 1. *n.* Anything that invites or attracts, as by offering pleasure or gain. 2. *v.* To attract or entice, especially into danger.

Mm

mag·net·ic field [mag·net′ik fēld] *n.* A region surrounding a magnet, an electromagnet, or a moving electric charge, in which a field of force is established.

mal·let [mal′it] *n.* A hammer, usually with a wooden head.

mam·moth [mam′əth] *n.* A large, now extinct animal related to the elephant.

mar·i·o·nette [mar′ē·ə·net′] *n.* A jointed figure or doll made to move by pulling strings, used in shows on small stages; puppet.

ma·son·ry [mā′sən·rē] *n.* A thing of stone, brick, etc., built by a mason.

May·day [mā′dā′] *n.* A request for help that is broadcast over a radio or some other electronic device.

may·or [mā′ər] *n.* The chief governing official of a city or town.

med·al [med′(ə)l] *n., pl.* **med·als** A small piece of metal with an image, writing, etc., on it, given as an award for an outstanding act or service.

melt·ing point [mel′ting point] *n.* The temperature at which any solid changes to a liquid.

me·sa [mā′sə] *n.* A hill or small plateau with a flat top and steep sides.

me·ter [mē′tər] *n.* The standard unit of length in the metric system, equal to 39.37 inches.

mi·cro·scope [mī′krə·skōp] *n.* An instrument, usually consisting of a combination of lenses, used to magnify objects too small to be seen or clearly observed by the naked eye.

mid·dling [mid′ling] *n. pl.* 1. Various products of medium size or quality. 2. The coarser part of ground grain.

min·er·al [min′ər·əl] *n.* A natural substance that is not a plant or animal and has a fairly definite physical and chemical make-up, such as quartz, coal, iron, etc.

mist [mist] *n.* A cloud of fine droplets of water.

moat [mōt] *n.* A ditch, usually full of water, around a castle, fortress, etc., used as a defense against attackers.

mod·el [mod′əl] *n.* A miniature copy or replica of an object.

mon·goose [mong′gōōs] *n., pl.* **mon·goos·es** A small animal of Asia and Africa. It resembles the ferret and preys on snakes and rats.

mourn·ing [môr′ning] *n.* A sorrowing; grieving, as an expression of sorrow for the dead.

munch [munch] *v.* To chew with a crunching noise—**munch′er** *n.*

mur·mur [mûr′mər] *v.* To complain, utter, or speak in a low, unclear, steady sound.

musk·rat [musk′rat] *n.* A mammal with glossy, brown fur and a strong scent.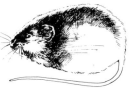

mys·ti·fy [mis′tə·fī] *v.* **mys·ti·fied** To puzzle or baffle; bewilder: Uncle Fred's sudden appearance *mystified* the family.

Nn

na·cre [nā′kər] *n.* Mother-of-pearl.

Na·po·le·on [nə·pō′lē·ən], 1769–1821, French military leader and dictator. Napoleon was defeated at Waterloo and imprisoned for the rest of his life.

nar·cis·sus [när·sis′əs] *n.* A spring plant that grows from a bulb and bears white and yellow flowers.

nat·u·ral·ist [nach′ər·əl·ist] *n.* A person who is trained in the study of nature, especially as related to the earth and living things.

nec·tar [nek′tər] *n.* A sweet liquid found in flowers, collected by bees to make honey.

nib·ble [nib′əl] *v.* To eat or bite in a quick, gentle way.

noo·dle [nōōd′(ə)l] *n.* A thin strip of dried dough, usually made with eggs.

numb [num] *adj.* Having no sensation or feeling.

Oo

oc·ta·gon [ok′tə·gon] *n.* A closed plane figure bounded by eight straight lines that form eight interior angles.

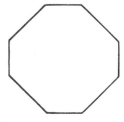

O·ki·na·wa [ō′kə·nä′wə] *n.* The largest island in the Ryukyus group, which is a part of Japan.

or·bit [ôr′bit] *n.* The path taken by a planet, comet, satellite, or space vehicle as it moves around its center of attraction.

or·deal [ôr·dēl′] *n.* A very difficult or trying experience.

ox·y·gen [ok′sə·jin] *n.* A colorless, tasteless, odorless gaseous element that is necessary for all life on earth.

oys·ter [ois′tər] *n.* A shellfish having a soft body within a rough, irregularly shaped shell in two parts hinged together.

Pp

pace [pās] 1. *n.* A step in walking or running. 2. *v.* To walk back and forth across: She always *paces* the floor when she is worried.

par·a·site [par′ə·sīt] *n.* A plant or animal that lives in or on another and gets its food and often shelter from the other, as a flea or mistletoe.

par·lor [pär′lər] *n.* A room for receiving visitors, entertaining guests, etc.

par·ti·cle [pär′ti·kəl] *n.* A very small part, piece, or amount; speck.

patent desk [pat′(ə)nt desk] *n.* A kind of desk that was developed, patented, and sold to schools.

pa·tient [pā′shənt] 1. *adj.* Able to wait for someone or something or to endure unpleasant things without complaining. 2. *n.* A person who is being treated for illness or injury.

pa·ti·o [pat′ē·ō] *n.* The open inner courtyard of a Spanish or Spanish-American building.

pause [pôz] 1. *v.* To stop temporarily. 2. *n.* A brief stop or short rest.

pearl [pûrl] *n.* A smooth, rounded, white or variously tinted deposit formed around a grain of sand or the like inside the shell of an oyster or other shellfish. It is valued as a gem.

pel·i·can [pel′i·kən] *n.* A large web-footed bird with a pouch on the lower jaw in which to carry captured fish.

perch [pûrch] 1. *n.* A pole, branch, or bar used as a roost for birds. 2. *v.* To sit on: The canary *perched* on my finger.

per·ma·nent [pûr′mən·ənt] *adj.* Continuing or intended to continue without change; lasting; enduring.

per·sim·mon [pər·sim′ən] *n.* A North American tree that bears reddish, plumlike fruit.

pe·ti·tion [pə·tish′ən] *n.* A formal, written request, often with many signatures, sent to a person or group in authority.

Phil·ip·pines [fil′ə·pēnz] *n.pl.* A country in the Pacific Ocean southeast of China, made up of over 7,000 islands.

pi·an·o [pē·an′ō] *n.* A large musical instrument played by striking keys on a keyboard with the fingers, each key making a padded hammer strike steel wires to produce a tone.

pick·er·el [pik′ər·əl] *n.* A fresh-water food fish related to the pike with a narrow snout and sharp teeth.

pit [pit] *n.* A hole or cavity in the ground, either natural or dug: They reached the *pit* of the mine.

plain [plān] *n.* An expanse of almost level, nearly treeless land; prairie.

plan·et [plan′it] *n.* Any of the bodies that move in orbits around the sun, with the exception of comets and meteors.

plead [plēd] *v.* **plead·ed** To ask earnestly; beg: As the ship sank, messages that *pleaded* for help were sent over the radio.

plumed [plo͞omd] *adj.* Decorated with feathers: Men in the 1700s sometimes wore *plumed* hats.

pole [pōl] *n.* Either end of the earth's axis; the North Pole or the South Pole.

po·li·o [pō′lē·ō] *n., informal* Poliomyelitis.

po·li·o·my·e·li·tis [pō′lē·ō·mī′ə·lī′tis] *n.* An acute, infectious virus disease most common in children and young adults, marked by inflammation of the spinal cord, and often followed by paralysis.

pop·lar [pop′lər] *n.* A tree related to the willow, that grows rapidly and has light, soft wood.

port·hole [pôrt′hōl] *n.* A small, windowlike opening in the side of a ship to admit air and light.

por·ti·co [pôr′ti·kō] *n.* An open space or walk covered by a roof held up by columns.

post·er [pōs′tər] *n.* A sign, printed notice, or advertisement posted in some public place.

prai·rie [prâr′ē] *n.* A large tract or area of more or less level, grassy land having few or no trees.

prai·rie dog [prâr′ē dog] *n.* A small rodent of the plains of North America that lives in large communities.

praise [prāz] *v.* To express approval or favor of someone or something.

prance [prans] *v.* To walk or move in a lively, proud way; to move with high steps, as a horse.

pres·sure [presh′ər] *n.* The force pushing against a surface per unit of area.

prop [prop] *n., informal* Short for property used in stage or film productions, such as furniture or special-effect models: The scenery and the *props* belonged to the film studio.

pro·pel·ler [prə·pel′ər] *n.* A device for pulling or pushing an aircraft or vessel through air or water by means of rotating blades set in their hub at a slant so that they bite into the air or water and thrust it back.

prov·i·dence [prov′ə·dəns] *n.* Someone or something that cares and protects.

pup·pet [pup′it] *n.* A small figure of a person or animal, usually with a cloth body and a solid head, fitting over and moved by the hand.

pu·ri·fy [pyo͞or′ə·fī] *v.* **pu·ri·fy·ing** To make or become pure or clean: Thunderstorms do a good job of *purifying* the air.

Qq

quar·ter [kwôr′tər] *n.* One of four equal parts that make up a whole.

quest [kwest] n. A seeking or looking for something; search.

Rr

rage [rāj] *v.* **rag·ing** To move or proceed with violence: The storm was *raging* up and down the coast.

range [rānj] *n.* A broad tract of land over which cattle, etc., roam and graze.

ra·ven [rā′vən] *n.* A large, black crow with shaggy throat feathers and a powerful beak.

re·al·i·ty [rē·al′ə·tē] *n.* An actual person, thing, or fact.

re·cep·tion [ri·sep′shən] *n.* A party at which guests are formally greeted.

re·con·sid·er [rē·kən·sid′ər] *v.* To think about something again, especially with the idea of changing one's mind.

reef [rēf] *n.* A ridge of sand, rocks, or coral at or near the surface of the water.

re·gret [ri·gret′] *v.* To feel sorrow or grief about.

reins [rānz] *n.pl.* Straps attached to the bit to control a horse or other animal while it is being ridden or driven.

re·lief [ri·lēf′] *n.* Lessening of or freeing from pain, a difficulty, etc.

rem·or·a [rem′ər·ə] *n.* Any of several small saltwater fish that have an oval sucking disc on their backs with which they cling to large fish and ships.

re·place [ri·plās′] *v.* **re·placed** To refill the space of: She *replaced* the light bulb.

re·ply [ri·plī′] *v.* **re·plied** To give an answer or response: Pilar *replied* by letter to the invitation.

rep·re·sent [rep′ri·zent′] *v.* To be the symbol or expression of; stand for: The letters of the alphabet *represent* sounds of speech.

re·qui·em shark [rek′wē·əm shärk] *n.* A family of sharks which includes the great white shark.

res·er·va·tion [rez′ər·vā′shən] *n.* A tract of government land reserved for a special purpose.

re·sound [ri·zound′] *v.* To be filled with sound or to echo back.

re·spect·ful [ri·spekt′fəl] *adj.* Showing esteem or honor; courteous. —**re·spect′ful·ly** *adv.*

re·strain [ri·strān′] *v.* **re·strained** To hold back; repress: Even though it made me angry, I *restrained* myself.

rhythm [rith′əm] *n.* The repetition of a beat, sound, accent, motion, etc., usually in a regular way.

rouse [rouz] *v.* **roused** To wake up from sleep, indifference, etc.: We *roused* ourselves out of our boredom and went to play tennis.

rub·bish [rub′ish] *n.* 1. Trash, garbage, or refuse: They threw the old tires on the *rubbish* heap. 2. Nonsense.

ru·ins [rōō′inz] *n.* The remains of something that has decayed or been destroyed.

rum·ble [rum′bəl] *v.* **rum·bled** To move or proceed making a low, heavy, rolling sound, as thunder: The trucks *rumbled* down the highway.

rum·ple [rum′pəl] *v.* **rum·pled** To wrinkle, mess, or crumple: He *rumpled* his clothing in packing.

Ss

Sac·a·ja·we·a [săc′ä·jä·wē′ä], 1787–1884, Shoshone interpreter; known in U.S. history as the principal guide of the Lewis and Clark Expedition to the Pacific Ocean. She lived much of her life in the Wind River country.

sa·fa·ri [sə·fä′rē] *n.* An expedition or journey in which something is sought.

sage [sāj] *n.* An herb related to mint, with gray-green leaves, used as a seasoning in food.

sa·la·mi [sə·lä′mē] *n.* A salted, spiced sausage, originally Italian.

sa·li·va [sə·lī′və] *n.* The liquid produced in the mouth; spit.

sat·el·lite [sat′ə·līt] *n.* A celestial body that revolves in an orbit around a larger celestial body.

sav·age [sav′ij] *adj.* Cruel, vicious, and violent.

sci·ence [sī′əns] *n.* Knowledge consisting of a systematic arrangement of facts and principles obtained through observation, experiment, and ordered thinking.

sci·en·tist [sī′ən·tist] *n.* A person expert in systematic thought and devoted to study.

scil·la [sil′ə] *n.* Any of a number of low, flowering plants of the lily family, grown for their blue or white blossoms.

scorn·ful [skôrn′fəl] *adj.* Full of or showing contempt.—**scorn′ful·ly** *adv.*

scour [skour] *v.* **scour·ing** To clean or brighten by washing and rubbing hard, as with sand or steel wool.

scroll [skrōl] *n.* A roll of parchment, paper, etc., especially one with writing on it.

scrump·tious [skrump′shəs] *adj., informal* Delightful; delicious; excellent.

scuff [skuf] *v.* To roughen or wear down the surface of, as by scraping:

The toes of my shoes *scuff* against the curb.—**scuffed** *adj.*

sedge [sej] *n.* Any of several coarse, grasslike plants that grow mainly in damp or swampy places.

seize [sēz] *v.* **seized** To take hold of suddenly and with force; grab; snatch.

sen·tence [sen′təns] *n.* The punishment pronounced upon a person convicted of a crime.

se·ri·ous [sir′ē·əs] *adj.* Grave; solemn; thoughtful.

ser·vice [sûr′vis] *n.* 1. Any work done or action performed for the benefit of another; assistance; benefit: to render *service* to a friend. 2. *(often pl.)* A useful work that does not produce a material object: the *services* of a doctor or lawyer. 3. Something that benefits or aids the public as a whole: bus *service;* electric *service.*

shark [shärk] *n.* Any of various long-bodied marine fishes, some very large, that have hard, rough skins and very sharp teeth. Sharks eat other fish, and some kinds will attack people.

sheep·ish [shē′pish] *adj.* Foolish, meek, or shy.—**sheep′ish·ly** *adv.*

shell·fish [shel′fish] *n.* Any animal that lives in the water and has a shell, as an oyster.

shiv·er [shiv′ər] *v.* To tremble, as with cold or fear; shake; quiver.

shock [shok] *n.* 1. A violent jolt or blow; sudden impact. 2. A sudden and severe upset of the mind or feelings, as in fright or great sorrow.

shriek [shrēk] *v.* **shriek·ing** To make a sharp, shrill outcry, scream, or sound: The police sirens were *shrieking* in the middle of the night.

shut·ter [shut′ər] *n.* A hinged panel for covering a window.

sig·na·ture [sig′nə·chər] *n.* The name of a person written by that person.

silk·en [sil′kən] *adj.* Like silk; smooth; glossy.

sil·ver·y [sil′vər·ē] *adj.* Like silver, as in color or luster.

singe [sinj] *v.* **singed** To burn slightly; scorch.

six·pence [siks′pəns] *n.* A British coin worth half a shilling, no longer in circulation.

skel·e·ton [skel′ə·tən] *n.* The supporting bony framework of the body of a vertebrate animal.

skid [skid] *v.* To slide sideways, as a car on an icy surface.

sky·scrap·er [skī′skrā·pər] *n.* A very high building.

slime [slīm] *n.* Any soft, moist, sticky substance that clings and often soils, as muck.

slops [slops] *n.* Waste food fed to pigs, etc.

sluice [slo͞os] *n.* An artificial channel for conducting water, equipped with a valve or gate to regulate the flow.

slump [slump] *v.* To stand, walk, or sit with a drooping posture.

smear [smir] 1. *v.* To blur or make indistinct. 2. *n.* A soiled spot, streak, etc., caused by smearing.

smoth·er [smuth′ər] *v.* **smoth·er·ing** To prevent or be prevented from getting air to breathe; suffocate.

snail [snāl] *n.* A small, slow-moving animal with a soft body and a spiral shell on its back into which it can pull itself.

snarl [snärl] *v.* **snarled** To growl, showing the teeth, as an angry or frightened dog: Fido *snarled* at the letter carrier.

sniff [snif] *v.* **sniffed** To breathe in through the nose in short, audible breaths: The fox lifted its nose and *sniffed* the air.

snoop·er [snoop′ər] *n., informal* One who looks or pries into things which are none of his or her business.

snor·kel [snôr′kəl] *n.* A tube attached to a skin diver's mask that makes it possible to breathe when a little under water.

snout [snout] *n.* The forward, projecting part of the head of many animals, usually including the nose and jaws.

snow·shoe [snō′shoo′] 1. *n.* A network of leather thongs set in a wooden frame and fastened on the foot in order to help a person walk on soft snow without sinking in. 2. *v.* To walk on snowshoes.

sod [sod] *n.* The top layer of the earth, especially when covered with grass.

so·lar sys·tem [sō′lər sis′təm] *n.* The sun and all the heavenly bodies that move in orbit around it.

sole [sōl] *n.* The bottom surface of a shoe, boot, stocking, etc.

sol·emn [sol′əm] *adj.* Majestic, impressive, and awe-inspiring. — **sol′emn·ly** *adv.*

sor·row [sor′ō] *n.* Sadness or distress of mind because of some loss or misfortune.

sou·ve·nir [soo′və·nir′] *n.* Something that is kept as a reminder of the past.

spa·ghet·ti [spə·get′ē] *n.* Long slender strings of flour paste, boiled as food.

spe·cial ef·fect [spesh′əl i·fekt′] *n.* Device used to create an illusion for either film or video.

splint [splint] *n.* A piece of wood or metal for holding the parts of a fractured bone in position.

sprain [sprān] *v.* **sprained** To cause a straining of the ligaments around a joint; wrench; twist: She *sprained* her ankle.

squawk [skwôk] 1. *v.* To give a shrill, harsh cry, as a parrot. 2. *n.* Such a shrill, harsh cry.

squint [skwint] *v.* To look with half-closed eyes, as into bright light.

stag·ger [stag′ər] *v.* **stag·ger·ing** To walk or run unsteadily; sway; reel.

sta·lac·tite [stə·lak′tīt] *n.* A slender, tapering column of mineral matter, chiefly limestone, hanging from the roof of a cave.

sta·lag·mite [stə·lag′mīt] *n.* A limestone column shaped like a cone rising from the floor of a cave.

stale [stāl] *adj.* Not fresh any longer; slightly changed or gone bad, as air, bread, etc.

star·tle [stär′təl] *v.* **star·tled** To frighten, surprise, or excite suddenly: The loud noise *startled* me.

stead·y [sted′ē] *adj.* Moving or acting regularly and without changes: a *steady* wind.

steam [stēm] *n.* The gas or vapor into which water is changed by boiling.

stew [st(y)ōō] *n.* Boiled food, especially a preparation of meat or fish and various vegetables, cooked together slowly.

stew·ard [st(y)ōō′ərd] *n.* A person who manages the property, finances, or other affairs of another person or persons.

stoop [stōōp] *n.* A small porch or platform at the entrance of a house.

stork [stôrk] *n.* Any of various large wading birds with long necks and long legs.

stout [stout] *adj.* Fat or thickset in body.

strag·gle [strag′əl] *v.* **strag·gled** To be spread unevenly about: Flowers *straggled* all over the garden.

strain [strān] *v.* To injure or damage by twisting, pulling.

stu·di·o [st(y)ōō′dē·ō] *n., pl.* **stu·di·os** 1. The place where an artist, musician, etc., works or teaches. 2. A place in which films, recordings, radio performances, etc., are made.

sub·sti·tute [sub′stə·t(y)ōōt] *n.* A person or thing that takes the place of someone or something else.

sub·way [sub′wā] *n.* An electric railroad that is mainly underground.

sulk [sulk] *v.* To be sullenly cross or ill-humored.

sup·posed to [sə·pōzd′ tōō] *v.* A phrase meaning to require.

sur·face [sûr′fis] *n.* The outer part or face of any solid body, or the upper level of a liquid.

swerve [swûrv] **swerv·ing** *v.* To turn or cause to turn aside from a course: We missed the dog by *swerving* our bicycles out of the way.

swift [swift] *n.* A bird that looks like a swallow and flies extremely fast.

swoop [swōōp] *v.* **swooped** To drop or descend suddenly: The bird *swooped* down on its prey.

sym·pho·ny or·ches·tra [sim′fə·nē ôr′kəs·trə] *n.* A large orchestra composed usually of people who play strings, brasses, woodwinds, and percussion instruments.

Tt

tal·ent·ed [tal′ən·tid] *adj.* Having natural aptitude or skill; gifted.

tan·gle [tang′gəl] *v.* **tan·gled** To twist or become twisted together into a confused mass.

tar·ry [tar′ē] *v.* To stay for a while; linger.

tax [taks] *n.* A charge paid by people, businesses, etc., for support of government in a city, county, state, or nation.

tech·nique [tek·nēk′] *n.* A way of or skill in handling tools, instruments, materials, or one's body in an art, science, sport, craft.

tet·a·nus [tet′ə·nəs] *n.* A disease marked by stiffening and spasms of the muscles, especially of the neck and jaw, caused by a bacterium that enters the body through a wound.

thaw [thô] *v.* To melt, as something frozen.

there's [thârz] There is.

ther·mos [thûr′məs] *n.* A bottle, jug, etc., for keeping liquids hot or cold by means of a vacuum surrounding an inner container.

thorn·bush [thôrn′bŏŏsh] *n.* A plant that bears thorns.

thrash [thrash] *v.* **thrash·ing** To make or cause to make violent swinging or twisting movements.

threat [thret] *n.* A warning or a promise that one intends to hurt or punish another person or thing.

tide [tīd] *n.* The periodic rise and fall of the surface of an ocean or of waters connected with the ocean, caused by the attraction of the sun and moon.

tilt [tilt] *v.* To incline at an angle; lean; tip.

tin·gly [ting′(ə)lē] *adj.* A prickly or tingling sensation.

ti·pi [tē′pē] *n.* (*Lakota Sioux word*) A cone-shaped tent, stretched across poles so that it is mobile.

tone-deaf [tōn′def] *adj.* Not able to distinguish between one pitch and another.

trade·mark [trād′märk′] *n.* A name or symbol used to distinguish one company's goods from those made or sold by others.

tram·ple [tram′pəl] *v.* **tram·pling** To walk heavily: The horse was *trampling* the flowers when they found him.

trap·pings [trap′ingz] *n., pl.* Very elaborate ornaments or garments.

tri·al [trī′əl] *n.* 1. The examination before a court of the charges made in a case in order to prove such charges either true or false. 2. The act of testing or proving by experience or use.

tro·phy [trō′fē] *n.* Something representing victory or success, as a cup awarded for an athletic achievement.

trough [trôf] *n.* A long, narrow, open container for holding food or water for animals.

trudge [truj] *v.* **trudg·ing** To walk wearily or with great effort; plod: They had been *trudging* for five miles when someone stopped to help.

trunk [trungk] *n.* The human body, apart from the head, neck, and limbs.

try·out [trī′out′] *n.* A test of ability, as of an actor or athlete: The *tryout* was a strain on everyone.

tum·ble [tum′bəl] *v.* **tum·bled** To roll, toss, or whirl about: The clothes all *tumbled* around inside the dryer.

tusk [tusk] *n.* One of the two very large teeth that stick out of the mouths of animals such as the elephant and the walrus: The elephant uses its *tusks* to protect itself.

twist [twist] *v.* To curve or bend. — **twist·ed** *adj.*

ty·rant [tī′rənt] *n.* A ruler having complete power.

Uu

un·dig·ni·fied [un·dig′nə·fīd] *adj.* Rowdy, sloppy to the point of losing respect.

u·ni·verse [yōō′nə·vûrs] *n.* The whole that is made up of everything that exists, including earth, sun, stars, planets, and outer space.

un·rea·son·a·ble [un·rē′zən·ə·bəl] *adj.* Not balanced or sensible.

ur·gent [ûr′jənt] *adj.* Needing or demanding prompt action or attention; pressing.

ush·er [ush′ər] *n.* A person who conducts people to their seats, as in a theater or church.

Vv

val·u·a·ble [val′y(ōō·)ə·bəl] 1. *adj.* Being worth a great deal: a *valuable* painting. 2. *n. (usually pl.)* Something worth much money, as jewelry: We must put the *valuables* in the safe before we leave.

valve [valv] *n.* Any device that regulates or controls the flow of a fluid or gas, as through a pipe.

van·ish [van′ish] *v.* **van·ished** To disappear suddenly from sight: The magician's rabbit *vanished* right before our eyes.

var·i·ous [vâr′ē·əs] *adj.* Different from one another; of different kinds.

vein [vān] *n., pl.* **veins** One of the muscular, tubelike vessels that carry blood back to the heart.

vel·vet [vel′vit] *n.* A cloth of silk, rayon, cotton, etc. with a thick, smooth pile on one side.

ve·ran·da [və·ran′də] *n.* A long, open, outdoor porch, usually roofed, along the outside of a building.

ver·dict [vûr′dikt] *n.* The decision of a jury after a trial: The *verdict* was "not guilty."

vi·o·lin [vī′ə·lin′] *n.* A musical instrument with a wooden body and four strings, played with a bow.

vit·tle [vit′əl] *n., pl.* **vit·tles** *archaic, informal* Food.

vul·ture [vul′chər] *n.* A large bird, usually with a naked head, that feeds mostly on decaying flesh.

Ww

wea·ry [wir′ē] *adj.* Tired; fatigued.

webbed [webd] *adj.* Having the toes united by folds of skin.

weep·ing wil·low [wē′ping wil′ō] *n.* One of a group of trees and shrubs having smooth branches, thin, flexible twigs which hang down, and long, narrow leaves.

whim·per [(h)wim′pər] *v.* To cry with low, mournful, broken sounds.

whin·ny [(h)win′ē] *n.* A gentle neigh made by a horse.

whir [(h)wûr] *v.* **whir·ring** To fly, move, or whirl with a hum or buzz: The engine was *whirring* softly as we waited at the stoplight.

whirl [(h)wûrl] *v.* **whirled, whirl·ing** To turn very fast with a circular motion; spin rapidly: The ranch hand *whirled* his lasso.

whit·tle [(h)wit′(ə)l] *v.* **whit·tling** To cut or shave bits from (wood, a stick, etc.): He spent his time *whittling* a squirrel from a stick.

whoa [(h)wō] *interj.* Stop! Stand still!—*Whoa* is used as a command to a horse.

whole·sale [hōl′sāl] *n.* The selling of goods in large quantities, especially to retail stores for resale to the public.

wield [wēld] *v.* To hold and use a weapon or tool; handle: She *wields* the cutting tool very skillfully.

wit·ness [wit′nis] *n.* A person who has seen or knows something and can give evidence concerning it.

wood·car·ver [wood-kär′vər] *n.* A person who is skilled in wood sculpture.

work·bench [wûrk′bench′] *n.* A heavy, strong table on which work is done, as by a carpenter.

wrig·gle [rig′əl] *v.* **wrig·gled** To twist or squirm: After an hour all the children *wriggled* in their chairs.

Yy

yip·py [yip′ē] *adj., informal* Nervous or active, as a small dog.

ACKNOWLEDGMENTS

For permission to adapt and reprint copyrighted materials, grateful acknowledgment is made to the following publishers, authors, and other copyright holders:

Barron's Educational Series, Inc., for "Albert Einstein" by Ibi Lepscky. Reprinted with respect to the first English language edition 1982 by Barron's Educational Series, Inc., 113 Crossways Park Drive, Woodbury, New York. From *Albert Einstein* by Ibi Lepscky. Copyright ©1982 Emme Edizioni.

The Belknap Press of Harvard University Press, for "A Bird Came Down the Walk" by Emily Dickinson. Reprinted by permission of the publishers and the Trustees of Amherst College from *The Poems of Emily Dickinson,* ed. by Thomas H. Johnson, Cambridge, Mass.: The Belknap Press of Harvard University Press, copyright ©1951, ©1955, 1979, 1983 by the President and Fellows of Harvard College.

The Curtis Publishing Company, for "Chuka's Hawk" by Elizabeth B. Whitmore from *Jack and Jill* magazine, copyright ©1964 by The Curtis Publishing Company. Adapted by permission of the publisher.

Delacorte Press, for "Something Strange on Vacation" adapted from *Something Queer on Vacation* by Elizabeth Levy. Copyright ©1980 by Elizabeth Levy. Reprinted by permission of Delacorte Press.

Doubleday & Company, Inc., for "Barefoot Days" from *Taxis and Toadstools* by Rachel Field, copyright 1926 by Doubleday & Co., Inc.; and for "Skyscrapers" from *Taxis and Toadstools* by Rachel Field, copyright 1924 by Yale University Press, reprinted by permission of Doubleday & Company, Inc.

E. P. Dutton, Inc., for "Snowshoe Trek to Otter River" adapted from *Snowshoe Trek to Otter River* by David Budbill, copyright ©1976 by David Budbill, reprinted by permission of the publisher, Dial Books for Young Readers, A Division of E. P. Dutton, Inc.; for "Running with Rachel" adapted from *Running with Rachel* by Frank and Jan Asch, copyright ©1979 by Frank and Jan Asch, reprinted by permission of the publisher, Dial Books for Young Readers, A Division of E. P. Dutton, Inc.; and for "The Case of the Treasure Map" from *Encyclopedia Brown Saves the Day* by Donald J. Sobol, copyright ©1970 by Donald J. Sobol, reprinted by permission of the publisher, E. P. Dutton, Inc.

Norma Millay Ellis, literary executor, for "Travel" by Edna St. Vincent Millay from *Collected Poems,* Harper & Row. Copyright 1921, 1948 by Edna St. Vincent Millay. Reprinted by permission of Norma Millay Ellis.

Four Winds Press, a division of Scholastic, Inc., for "True Adventures of Eugenie Clark: Shark Lady," adapted by permission of Four Winds Press, a division of Scholastic, Inc., from *True Adventures of Eugenie Clark: Shark Lady* by Ann McGovern, copyright ©1978 by Ann McGovern; and for "Sound of Sunshine, Sound of Rain" adapted by permission of Four Winds Press, a division of Scholastic, Inc., from *Sound of Sunshine, Sound of Rain* by Florence Parry Heide, copyright ©1979 by Florence Parry Heide, originally published by Parents Magazine Press.

Free To Be Foundation, Inc., for "The Southpaw" by Judith Viorst, from *Free to Be . . . You and Me* published by McGraw-Hill. Copyright ©1974 by Free To Be Foundation, Inc.

Harper & Row, Publishers, Inc., for "Rain Sizes" from *The Reason for the Pelican* by John Ciardi (J. B. Lippincott Co.), copyright ©1959 by John Ciardi; for "The Night Will Never Stay" from *Eleanor Farjeon's Poems for Children* (J. B. Lippincott Co.), copyright 1951 by Eleanor Farjeon; for "The Wheel on the School," adapted text from pp. 15-25 in *The Wheel on the School* by Meindert DeJong, copyright 1954 by Meindert DeJong; for "The Long Winter" from pp. 84-91 in *The Long Winter* by Laura Ingalls Wilder, copyright 1940 by Laura Ingalls Wilder, renewed 1968 by Roger L. MacBride; and for text and art of "Escape" from *Charlotte's Web* by E. B.

White, illustrated by Garth Williams, copyright 1952, 1980 by E. B. White, illustration copyright renewed 1980 by Garth Williams, all by permission of Harper & Row, Publishers, Inc.

Helen Hoke Associates, for "The Cat Who Became a Poet" by Margaret Mahy. © Margaret Mahy, 1977. First appeared in *Nonstop Nonsense* by Margaret Mahy, published by J. M. Dent & Sons, Ltd. Reprinted by permission of Helen Hoke Associates.

Holt, Rinehart and Winston, Publishers, for "Grand Papa and Ellen Aroon," adapted from *Grand Papa and Ellen Aroon* by F. N. Monjo, copyright ©1974 by F. N. Monjo and Louise L. Monjo; and for "The Stars in the Sky" adapted from *The Maid of the North* by Ethel Johnston Phelps, copyright ©1981 by Ethel Johnston Phelps, both reprinted by permission of Holt, Rinehart and Winston, Publishers.

Alfred A. Knopf, Inc., for "In Time of Silver Rain" by Langston Hughes. Copyright 1938 and renewed 1966 by Langston Hughes. Reprinted from *Selected Poems of Langston Hughes* by permission of Alfred A. Knopf, Inc.

Little, Brown and Company, for "All Except Sammy" from *All Except Sammy* by Gladys Yessayan Cretan. Copyright ©1966 by Gladys Yessayan Cretan. By permission of Little, Brown and Company in association with the Atlantic Monthly Press.

McGraw-Hill Book Company, for "Miss Pickerel Goes to Mars" by Ellen MacGregor. Copyright 1951 by Robert Noble MacGregor and John MacGregor. Copyright ©1962 by McGraw-Hill Book Company. Used by permission of McGraw-Hill Book Company.

Macmillan Publishing Co., Inc., for "Skating" from *Pillicock Hill* by Herbert Asquith. Copyright ©1926 by Macmillan Publishing Co., Inc. Used by permission of the publisher.

Irving R. Melbo, author, for "Strange Black Smoke." Used by permission of the author.

Eve Merriam, author, for "Where Is a Poem?" from *There Is No Rhyme for Silver* by Eve Merriam. Copyright ©1962 by Eve Merriam. Reprinted by permission of the author.

Julian Messner, a division of Simon & Schuster, Inc., for "Melindy's Medal" by Georgene Faulkner and John Becker. Copyright ©1945 by Georgene Faulkner and John Becker, renewed ©1972 by Perry John Ten Hoors and John Faulkner. Reprinted by permission of Julian Messner, a division of Simon & Schuster, Inc.

Modern Curriculum Press, for "The Solar System" from *The Solar System* by Isaac Asimov. Copyright ©1975 by Isaac Asimov. Used by permission of Modern Curriculum Press.

William Morrow & Co., for excerpts from pp. 11, 28-33, 47, 48, and 71-72 in *Animal Tools* by George F. Mason, copyright ©1951 by George F. Mason, adapted by permission of William Morrow & Co.; and for excerpts from pp. 74-92 in *Thank You, Jackie Robinson* by Barbara Cohen, copyright ©1974 by Barbara Cohen, adapted by permission of Lothrop, Lee & Shepard Books (A Division of William Morrow & Co.).

National Wildlife Federation, for "My Mom Is a Woodcarver" by Becky Brown as told to Sallie Luther. Copyright 1981 National Wildlife Federation. Adapted from the August 1981 issue of *Ranger Rick* magazine, with permission of the publisher, National Wildlife Federation.

The New Yorker Magazine, Inc., for "Catalogue" by Rosalie Moore. Reprinted by permission; ©1940, 1968 The New Yorker Magazine, Inc.

Price/Stern/Sloan, Publishers, Inc., for "The Muffin Muncher" adapted and reprinted from *The Muffin Muncher* by Stephen Cosgrove. Copyright ©1974 by Stephen Cosgrove. Published by Price/Stern/Sloan, Publishers, Inc., Los Angeles. Reprinted with permission.

The Saturday Evening Post Company, for "The Treasure of Sumiko's Bay" by Barbara Chamberlain from *Jack and Jill* magazine, copyright ©1975 by The Saturday Evening Post Company, Indianapolis, Indiana. Adapted by permission of the publisher.

Virginia Driving Hawk Sneve, author, for "The Medicine Bag." Copyright ©1975 by Virginia Driving Hawk Sneve. Used by permission of the author.

Franklin Watts, Inc., for "City Hall" adapted from *Project Cat* by Nellie Burchardt, copyright ©1966 by Franklin Watts, Inc. Used by permission of the publisher.

Viking Penguin, Inc., for "Einstein Anderson Makes Up for Lost Time" from *Einstein Anderson Makes Up for Lost Time* by Seymour Simon. Copyright ©1981 by Seymour Simon. Adapted by permission of Viking Penguin, Inc.

Grateful acknowledgment is made to the following for illustrations, photographs, and reproductions on the pages indicated:

Frank Ahern 254-259; Ellen Blonder 388-390; Canadian Film Board 35; Randy Chewning 28, 50, 68, 94, 115, 142, 176, 193, 230, 261, 277, 302, 328, 350, 380, 406, 423, 450; Floyd Cooper title page, copyright page, 12-13, 72-73, 146-147, 234-235, 306-308, 310-311, 313, 314, 316, 319, 321, 384-385, 446, 448; Culture Pearl Association of America in Japan 81; Jim Cummins 74, 77-79, 83, 354, 372, 375, 377, 379; David and Anne Doubilet 222, 225-226, 229; Michael Durbin 472, 475-478, 481-482, 485-487, 489, 491, 493, 495, 497, 499; Linda Edwards 60, 63-64, 66-67; Four By Five Southwest 34; Courtesy of Franklin D. Roosevelt Library 414-415; Gayla Taylor Goodell 52, 55-57, 59, 386-387; Historical Pictures Service, Chicago 412 (bottom); Roger F. Huebner 102, 105-106, 109, 111, 113, 416-421; Bryan Jowers 356; Mary Knowles 210-211, 213, 215-216, 219-220; Patrick Maloney 148, 150, 152, 155-156, 158, 161-162; Lyle Miller 122, 124, 126, 129, 131, 133-135, 137, 139, 141; Terra Muzick 252-253, 272, 275, 300-301; Amy Myers 221; National Aeronautics and Space Administration 180-185, 237-238, 241-243; National Baseball Hall of Fame and Museum 200, 203-204; Robert Phillips 163, 352-353; Ron Russell 178; Vera Rosenberry 96-101; Maurice Sendak 84, 86-87, 89, 91-93; Bill Shires 245, 247-248, 251, 331-332, 335, 339-341, 343, 358, 361-362, 364, 367, 371; Clyde H. Smith 322, 324-327; Philip Smith 14, 16-17, 19, 36, 38, 41-42, 45, 47, 49, 164, 167-168, 171-173, 175, 262, 264, 267, 269, 271, 454, 457, 459, 461-462, 464-466, 469; Courtesy of Margaret Suckley 411; United Nations 413; United Press International 198, 207, 412 (top); U.S. National Park Service 30, 32; Garth Williams 424, 426, 428-430, 433-434, 438, 445; Mike Wimmer 22, 25, 27, 70-71, 119, 121, 194, 209, 394, 397, 399, 401-403, 405, 408; Darrell Wiskur 346, 348-349.

The glossary illustrations are by Mike Wimmer.